ORDINARY D

Icon Entertainment International

presents

A film by Thaddeus O'Sullivan

A Little Bird Production in association
with Tatfilm and Trigger Street Productions

Produced in association with Miramax Films
Bord Scannán na hÉireann/The Irish Film Board
The Greenlight Fund
Filmstiftung NRW

Ordinary Decent Criminal

Gerard Stembridge

HEADLINE

First published in paperback in 2000
by HEADLINE BOOK PUBLISHING

10 9 8 7 6 5 4 3 2 1

ISBN 0 7472 6205 5

Typeset by
Letterpart Limited, Reigate, Surrey

Printed and bound in Great Britain by
Clays Ltd, St Ives plc

HEADLINE BOOK PUBLISHING
A division of Hodder Headline PLC
338 Euston Road
London NW1 3BH
www.headline.co.uk
www.hodderheadline.com

Contents

Introduction

The World According to Michael Lynch

As a Dublin schoolboy, most of my education was accomplished with the loose end of a leather belt. The Christian Brothers at Westland Row beat the lard out of us day in, day out. No one complained about that. But I still recall one of their enlightened 'initiatives' for transforming us into better persons: the elocution lesson. For this they brought in the battle-hardened Mrs Johnston, a retired schoolteacher. After weeks of frustration, little Harry Steers, a gurrier from Ringsend, finally rebelled and took her on with a bottle of Parazone. I remember the two of them rolling about the floor, arms wrapped around one another in a vicious embrace. We cheered the elegant delivery of his message, for we knew in our hearts that Harry was right.

The Irish have resisted most attempts at 'improvement' by priests and politicians and the like. I think the principal character of *Ordinary Decent Criminal*, Michael Lynch, embodies the resentment that is a consequence of such a relationship with authority. Michael is a robber of candy bars as well as gold bars. The distinction is immaterial so long as he can leave his fingerprints everywhere, for to be recognised is everything. If there's no fun, it's not worth doing, and the pleasure lies in offending the self-righteousness of authoritarian institutions – in Michael's case the Gardai, the social services, Interpol, the grandees of the art establishment . . .

Fair play. He is the rebel – part criminal mastermind, part delinquent schoolboy – who appeals to the Harry Steers in all of us; that voice we silence in the interests of remaining more-or-less law-abiding citizens. (I say more-or-less because we should remember that Michael Lynch's Ireland is a country on the make, where only a few years ago the government declared not one but two moratoria on unpaid taxes, such was the scale of the problem.)

We should find no excuses for the delinquent motivation behind his life of crime. Indeed, Michael doesn't. Even the urban grime and deprivation of his childhood is transmuted into a swashbuckling bedtime tale of Irish resistance and heroism for the benefit of his children. The only truth for Michael is the truth that suits his book.

Michael Lynch started out, of course, as a real-life character: a well-known Dublin gangster called Martin Cahill. The actual events of Cahill's life have already been set out in John Boorman's biopic, *The General*. Our own script moved, in successive drafts, away from the reality of Cahill's world towards the fictional universe imagined and ordered by the fictional Lynch, who never deferred to anyone older or wiser or better.

In a parable of this sort, such hubris must inevitably lead to nemesis. The real Martin Cahill died at the hands of an IRA faction (supposedly) for refusing to divvy up the spoils. This was the perfect demise, worthy of a Greek drama. But since real life is not always so obliging, in our own ending the reverse happens. Lynch engineers the demise of Higgins, the IRA man, in a police shoot-out at the Metropolitan Bank. Having sized-up Higgins as a plausible physical double, he forces him out in front of police guns, and in the ensuing confusion (this is the second 'Lynch' to appear) Higgins is cut down in a hail of enthusiastic gunfire from the Gardai.

In the finished version of the film (different in this script), Noel smells a rat and holds his fire. He knows that Lynch has escaped, but chooses to allow the system to bury the wrong man, for he also knows that in the execution of his final scam, Lynch has scored a Pyrrhic victory. Exiled amid the bogs and mists of the West of Ireland, and deprived of the media attention that has serviced his myth-making, what is he after all? A dog without a tail. I like the painful compromises of this version, which has its own truth. For *magna est veritas et prevalebit* – or, in the Flann O'Brien translation, 'the truth does be bitter'.

Thaddeus O'Sullivan
1999

EXT. DUBLIN STREETS – DAY

OVER CREDITS

A Kawasaki motorcycle speeds through Dublin city streets. Michael Lynch is forty. He rides his Kawasaki with ease and command. He owns these streets. Though his face is covered with a crash-helmet and a balaclava, we see the brightness in his eyes and an occasional grin that reveals confidence and charm. He approaches his destination. Dole Office.

For the next ten minutes of screen time, we do not see Michael's face. Always masked or hooded, by the time it is revealed we will feel we know him well.

EXT. DUBLIN STREETS – DAY

Michael and Tony, hooded, check their watches. Just after ten o'clock. They approach a quiet bank. There is one Man waiting. He blanches when he sees two masked men walk towards him. They smile at him.

MICHAEL

How's it going?

MAN

(very nervous)

Great – ah, lovely day.

MICHAEL

(glances at his watch)

Never on time, are they?

MAN

No, no. They're desperate, sure. Desperate, desperate altogether.

Someone inside is unlocking the door. Michael takes a gun out and points it at the Man.

MICHAEL

Try another branch.

The Man runs. The door opens. The Girl's happy morning face changes as Michael and Tony push her backwards into the bank.

Morning. A withdrawal, please.

EXT. STREET – DAY

JUMP CUT

Michael and Tony open the door and step out with a full bag. Michael now has the key and locks the door of the bank, leaving the key in the lock.

*[EXT. STREET, BRIDEWELL – DAY

* Cut from completed film.

The Kawasaki comes up the street. It slows down and stops where Michael's car is stopped in traffic. Stevie is following a prearranged route so they know where to find him.

Michael gets off the bike and opens the driver's door of the car as Tony rides off. Stevie moves to the passenger seat. Michael hands him the bag of money and takes off the crash-helmet.

MICHAEL

Hold on.

Michael reaches into the bag. Pulls out a wad of notes.

Legal expenses.

Stevie doesn't like Michael's attitude doing this. As he zips up the bag and gets out, hood up, he mutters:

STEVIE

You could write him a cheque?

He walks through the traffic and disappears up a side-street. Michael smirks after him and drives away.]

INT./EXT. CAR AT FOUR COURTS – DAY

Michael pulls up outside the courthouse. His solicitor Brian sits in. Michael's hooded state causes no surprise.

BRIAN

Harrison will defend the bail application, maybe even take the trial. But he insists on two thousand pound in cash—

MICHAEL

(shocked)

For a morning's work?

BRIAN

—up front. As in now, before we go in.

MICHAEL

The bollix. You mean he doesn't trust me.

BRIAN

Here he is, Michael. He's worth it.

MICHAEL

So, you're saying give him the cash. Fair enough.

They get out as Harrison approaches in a wig and gown.

HARRISON

Morning. It's nearly time.

(sotto voce)

Are we in funds?

MICHAEL

You mean the cash. I'll give it to you right here, I don't mind.

Michael goes for his pocket. Enjoys the horrified reaction.

HARRISON

No, no, no. Ah, not here, Mr Lynch. Come with me. And you will be taking that off in the courtroom – won't you?

INT. COURT – DAY

Harrison is in fine sincere form. He really is good. Michael has taken the balaclava off. But his face is still not seen.

HARRISON

. . . The prosecution's claim that they fear my client might flee the jurisdiction while on bail has no foundation. Mr Lynch has never ever left this country. He doesn't even hold a passport. It's not an exaggeration to suggest that it would break his heart to leave his beloved Dublin. Especially when, if I may remind your honour, that Mr Lynch's lovely little daughter Breda will be making her First Holy Communion very soon and surely it would be tragic if her father could not be with her on that day.

The Judge is clearly impressed by this point.

The State can offer no cause in law or in justice, why this quiet, unassuming, clean-living teetotaller should have his bail rescinded . . .

EXT. FOUR COURTS – DAY

Michael, hooded again, is first out of the court building followed by Harrison and Brian. A horde of journalists and photographers descend on Michael.

JOURNALIST 1

How does it feel to be the most wanted man in Ireland?

JOURNALIST 2

Why do you hide your face if you're innocent?

JOURNALIST 3

You enjoy making the Gardai look thick, don't you?

Michael enjoys this. He spots Barry and other detectives at the bottom of the steps. He turns to the journalists.

MICHAEL

Hold on now a minute, lads; hold 'til I tell you. Don't ever think the Gardai are thick because that'd be a big mistake. You'd be wrong. The Gardai are anything but thick . . .

A few chuckles.

No, no, I'm serious now. Mark my words; in fact I think the Gardai are very, very clever.

He walks on. The horde follow. As Michael reaches the bottom of the steps, Barry and Con step forward.

BARRY

Are you Michael Lynch?

MICHAEL

(to journalists, deadpan)

See what I mean – brains, you see.

BRIAN

Excuse me, I am Mr Lynch's solicitor and—

BARRY

I'm detaining you on suspicion of possessing illegal substances under the Misuse of Drugs Act.

As he speaks, Con and another detective grab Michael.

BRIAN

Now hold on.

CON

Here's the warrant.

Michael begins to struggle.

MICHAEL

I know what yous want – you want to strip search me, don't you, you dirty perverts—

CON

Come on, Lynch—

MICHAEL

You think you'll humble me, do you?

BARRY

You're under arrest.

MICHAEL

You can go as low as you like. I'll go lower.

He begins to pull his clothes off. The detectives did not expect this. The photographers move in. The detectives desperately try to stop him getting his clothes off.

You see what they do to innocent people.

Peeling off his trousers. He is wearing Mickey Mouse boxer shorts.

Dirty perverts getting their rocks off. Getting a feel. This is what I have to put up with. See him trying to grab my balls, you queer.

The trousers are now off. The detectives begin to back off. Michael dances around.

Look – drugs – where are the drugs? I've never had drugs in me life and everyone knows it. Come over and shove your hand up me hole. Come on, find some drugs.

Michael is now naked except for his masked face. As the cameras keep clicking and flashing, Barry and Con can take it no more. To jeers from the crowd, they get back into their cars and drive off quickly. Michael relaxes and grins.

INT. MICHAEL'S HOUSE – EVENING

The front page of the Evening Herald. *A photo of Michael masked. Huge headline: CRIME BOSS REVEALS EVERYTHING EXCEPT HIS FACE.*

Christine looks up from the paper. A hint of a grin.

CHRISTINE

Do you want any more, love?

A close-up of Michael's face for the first time. He is serenely munching dinner.

MICHAEL

No, that's grand. Unless there's dessert.

CHRISTINE

'Course there is.

Christine goes to get dessert. Michael sits back and rubs his stomach contentedly. Three of his children are at the table with him. Breda, Shane and Tommy, a sparky eight-year-old who points at a piece of steak left on Michael's plate.

TOMMY

Da, can I finish that?

MICHAEL

'Course you can – waste not, want not.

Michael tosses Tommy the piece of meat. He catches and eats it. Christine returns with a tray of lemonade and cream cakes. As she puts them on the table, the children grab. Christine stops them.

CHRISTINE

Ah, ah – your father first. Who earns the money in this house?

CHILDREN

(bored chorus)

Da does.

MICHAEL

(taking a cake)

Ah, sure, they're grand. There's loads for everyone.

CHRISTINE

(pouring lemonade)

No, they have to learn.

Giving Tommy his lemonade, she sees him chewing steak.

Ah Michael, you didn't give him a bit of your steak, did you? You know the way all that red meat makes him hyper.

Tommy is guzzling lemonade.

MICHAEL

Sorry, sorry, wasn't thinking.

CHRISTINE

(to Tommy)

You just better go to bed when you're told to tonight, do you hear. And no giddyacting.

INT./EXT. CAR/STREETS – DAY

Michael rides up the road, still pursued. He spots the family car coming the other way. They both pull up. Christine, Lisa and the children pile out.

CON

(off)

Is that them? Is that the two sisters?

BARRY

(off)

Sure is. The family that lays together stays together, ha?

CON

(off)

Jaze, they're nice though, both of them. Bet he was glad he didn't have to choose between 'em, wha'?

The kids jump around Michael. A happy family scene.

MICHAEL

Sorry I'm late. A bit of a hold-up.

He nods slightly towards the unmarked Garda car.

Now I have to show someone round the town.

CHRISTINE

You're grand. See you tonight.

Michael takes the keys, kisses both women and gets in the car. He dips briefly below the dashboard and pops up again with the crash-helmet off and his hood now up disguising his face.

BARRY

(off)

Ah give us a look at your face, ye fuck.

Michael gives Lisa his crash-helmet.

MICHAEL

(to the kids)

Behave yourselves, do you hear me? Do what your mothers tell you.

The kids all shout 'Bye Da,' and he drives off. The unmarked car takes off also.

LISA/CHRISTINE

Bastards.

LISA

(hops on the bike)

I'll call round later, so. Collect Eddie and Rory.

CHRISTINE

Grand.

The kids clamour for a ride on the bike. 'Give us a go,' 'Take me Ma,' 'Go on, give us a backer.'

LISA

No. No, I said. You know I won't take you without a crash-helmet. It's against the law.

EXT. DUBLIN STREET – DAY

Michael, in his car, is followed by detectives.

EXT. MOTORWAY – DAY

The cars reach the outskirts of Dublin, the Wicklow Hills in the distance.

EXT. DUBLIN MOUNTAINS – DUSK

The sun is setting in a remote part of the mountains as the two lone cars plough on.

CON

(off)

So, like, OK, he knows we're after him, well then he can see that there's no way he can shake us off – not out here anyway – right? So what's the point?

BARRY

(off)

Hello, listen – Now we're up the Sally Gap about five miles east of Lara and ten from Bray.

CONTROL

(off)

You're where? You mean he hasn't—

BARRY

(off)

He's driving non-stop. We're getting very low. Where's the nearest service station?

CONTROL

(off)

Jesus. Right, be back to you.

Michael glances at his fuel gauge. Almost empty. He pulls up and gets out.

BARRY

(off)

Hold on – hold on – this is it now. Here we go.

Michael opens the boot and takes out a five-gallon drum of petrol. He looks directly at the unmarked car, parked a hundred yards behind. He waves the drum at them, cheerfully. He fills his tank. Barry and Con watch in horror.

Ah, for fuck's – Hello, hello, ah quick, hello – Control!

CONTROL

(off)

Ok lads, your nearest service station is a good ten miles, maybe more. North-east on the Bray road.

Michael gets back into his car. Against the backdrop of the lonely hills, Michael's car drives away, leaving Barry and Con on the hillside as Control continues giving instructions.

If you're facing Lara now, you have to turn back and go towards Brittas until you hit the coast road. Then turn left for Bray and there's an Esso on the left three miles outside the town. But you have to move fairly fast because it closes at ten o'clock . . .

EXT. WERBURGH STREET – DAY

Michael parks outside the Dole Office. As he gets off his bike he suddenly looks directly over at a certain car. Inside that car are Barry and Con.

BARRY

Here comes Lynch. Motorbike, balaclava. The usual old circus.

CONTROL

(off)

Right, Unit 4, begin covert surveillance.

Michael just looks and grins under his mask. He enters the Dole Office.

BARRY

Look at him. Getting free money off the State, the cheeky fuck.

INT. DOLE OFFICE – DAY

A miserable Victorian high-ceilinged building with caged windows. Queues of unemployed wait to collect their weekly allowance. Michael in the queue nudges Tony.

MICHAEL

Where would you be without the Social Welfare, ha?

TONY

Couldn't agree more, Michael – a vital few bob.

MICHAEL

The thing is, Tony, what it means to our wives and kids.

TONY

(to the Clerk as he collects his money)

Sure, I know. It's the difference between eating or not eating sometimes.

MICHAEL

You said it, pal. Good luck.

As Tony turns away he takes Michael's crash-helmet from him. Michael approaches the Clerk. Big smile.

MICHAEL

Michael Lynch. And how are you today?

The Clerk, a slight, nervous thirty-year-old, knows who he is. It's a routine. He smiles an anxious smile back.

Tony reaches the main door. He quickly slips on a balaclava and Michael's crash-helmet. Another man, Stevie, mid-thirties, casually hands him a jacket exactly like Michael's. Tony puts it on and goes out the door: Michael to the life.

EXT. WERBURGH STREET – DAY

It seems like Michael has emerged from the Dole Office. So when Tony gets on the Kawasaki and screeches off at speed, Barry and Con follow in the unmarked car.

BARRY

(To intercom)

OK, he's off on his travels. We're up his hole, Control.

Stevie watches from the Dole Office doorway.

INT. DOLE OFFICE – DAY

MICHAEL

(gathering his money)

You're a gentleman, do you know that? It's fellahs like you make the world go round.

He smiles at the relieved Clerk, and walks away.

EXT. WERBURGH STREET – DAY

Stevie and Michael now step out. Stevie dons a balaclava too. They go round a corner where Billy (Michael's young brother) and Alec (the twenty-year-old wheelsman) are waiting in a car. Without a word but at speed, Billy throws Michael a different jacket and a crash-helmet to each of them. Then he takes out two pump-action rifles.

MICHAEL
(to Billy)
Thanks, little fellah.

Stevie and Michael turn and walk back around the corner into the Dole Office.

INT. DOLE OFFICE – DAY

Stevie and Michael enter casually but suddenly explode into action. Shouting, guns raised, they force everyone on to the floor. A nervous Billy, also armed, guards the doorway.

Michael returns to his own hatch. He silently gestures to the Clerk, who instantly starts to gather up money.

INT./EXT. CAR/STREETS – DAY

Tony (disguised as Michael) weaves gently through the traffic making sure the unmarked police car doesn't lose him.

BARRY
I'll say one thing for him. He sticks to the speed limit.

EXT. WERBURGH STREET – DAY

34c
46

Stevie and Michael burst out of the Dole Office. Billy follows. Alec has the car running and takes off at great speed.

INT./EXT. CAR/STREETS – DAY

Tony on the Kawasaki glances at his watch and suddenly takes off at speed. The unmarked car responds.

BARRY

(to intercom)

Oho – here we go – he's off. Put the foot down, Con. Something happening, Control.

CONTROL

(off)

You're telling me there is. There's a report of a robbery in Werburgh Street Dole Office.

BARRY

(to intercom)

Ah, fuck; we're only after – what? Will we go back?

*[EXT. RATHMINES GARDA STATION – DAY

The getaway car screeches to a halt outside Rathmines Garda Station. Michael jumps out, wearing his own jacket again, still wearing the balaclava.

STEVIE

Hey, Michael.

Michael looks back. Stevie tosses him a crash-helmet.

* Cut from completed film.

MICHAEL

Thanks – see ye tomorrow.

He strolls into the Garda Station.

INT. RATHMINES GARDA STATION – DAY

Michael approaches the desk. He offers his licence and insurance to the Desk Sergeant.

MICHAEL

Michael Lynch.

SERGEANT

I know who you are.

MICHAEL

I want to complain about a barking dog.

Sergeant gives him a look. Knows his form.

SERGEANT

Who're you after robbing, Lynch?

MICHAEL

Sorry? It's the neighbour's, Sergeant. She's a right bitch. Keeps me awake all night, you know—

SERGEANT

Do you think we're fools, Lynch?

MICHAEL

(imitating dog)

WOUGH! WOUGH! WOUGH! Real loud, you know, persistent . . .

EXT. RATHMINES GARDA STATION – DAY

Tony now arrives at the police station, still followed by the unmarked car. He goes inside. Barry and Con look at each other, puzzled.

BARRY

(off)

Ah, Control. He's after going into Headquarters. What's that about?

CONTROL

(off)

An alibi. That's what it's about. Hold on . . .

INT. RATHMINES GARDA STATION TOILETS – DAY

Tony, head down, walks into the toilets. He bumps into a genial Old Garda who is on his way out.

INT. TOILETS – DAY

Tony goes into a cubicle. He closes the door and throws the motorcycle key over the top, into the next cubicle.

The door of the other cubicle opens and Michael walks out, balaclava and helmet on, keys in hand.

INT. OUTSIDE TOILETS – DAY

As Michael goes, he passes the astonished Old Garda, who has stopped to light up a cigarette.

GARDA

Jesus, that was fast!

EXT. RATHMINES GARDA STATION – DAY

The real Michael now steps out and mounts his Kawasaki.

CONTROL

(off)

Desk Sergeant says he was in to complain about a barking dog. Taking the mickey as usual. Don't let him out of your sights, do you hear me?

He rides off. Barry and Con follow.

INT. MICHAEL'S HOME – NIGHT

Michael arrives home. Upstairs are the sounds of Christine talking to the boys in their bedroom. Christine comes down.

CHRISTINE

They're saying you promised to tell them a story.

MICHAEL

No way.

CHRISTINE

Well go and sort it, will you. They're sitting up waiting.

MICHAEL

The chancers.]

INT. BOYS' BEDROOM – NIGHT

Michael enters. The boys are indeed sitting up waiting.

MICHAEL

I never promised you a story.

TOMMY

You did. You did so, Da.

MICHAEL

What did I tell you about lying?

TOMMY

I'm to lie to everyone except you and Ma.

SHANE

And us.

TOMMY

Oh yeah, and Auntie Lisa.

MICHAEL

And the whole family. You never lie to anyone in the family.

SHANE

Tell us a story about Hollyfield, Da. When the whole family was living together in the one place.

MICHAEL

Fair enough – you want to hear the whole thing?

TOMMY

From the start.

Michael settles himself on the floor between the two beds. He begins to imagine.

MICHAEL

OK. Long, long ago, years ago before you were born and your Ma and me and Auntie Lisa were very young, we all lived in a place called Hollyfield, and everyone was in the one place, all our grannies and grandads and brothers and sisters and all our pals. It was brilliant. It was like a big hotel specially built for us and all our mates . . .

EXT. HOLLYFIELD – NIGHT

The slum flats of Hollyfield, seen through fairy-tale eyes. Teeming with people, kids running round, women hanging out of windows gossiping, men standing around, smoking, messing, playing toss-penny.

MICHAEL

(off)

. . . and we were always looking out for each other . . .

Young Michael moves from door to door. At each door a hand comes out and Michael hands over a carton of cigarettes.

. . . everyone had a special talent, and we'd all know the best person to go to for whatever thing we needed . . .

Young Tony opens his jacket. Assorted tins tumble on to a table.

EXT. OVERHEAD – HOLLYFIELD – NIGHT

MICHAEL

(off)

And when I was small I used to think that God was smiling down on us, putting a special glow around us so that we could do as we pleased, go about our business with no one getting in our way . . . and it would never change.

A squad car pulls up. Ugly gorilla-like versions of Noel and Barry step out. Stones rain on them. They retreat hastily.

And whenever anyone tried to interfere with us, they didn't stand a chance. We'd stand together and we were too strong for them.

TOMMY

(off)

Tell us about the bailiffs, Da.

MICHAEL

I'm coming to it – I'm coming to it. All right so. The bailiffs.

EXT. HOLLYFIELD – NIGHT

The evil Bailiffs stand at the gate of Hollyfield.

MICHAEL

(off)

There were loads of them and they were huge. And you know what bailiffs are?

SHANE

(off)

They're like the Gardai, only worse.

MICHAEL

(off)

Much worse. So one day – this was when you were a baby, Shane – this one day I was coming home after working hard all day . . .

Young Michael walks on to Hollyfield, his jacket bulging. He stops in horror. The Bailiffs are beating down the door of the flats with lump hammers. Terrified occupants cower at windows.

. . . and I saw them attacking our homes. Loads of these big bastards, and they had hammers and knives and all sorts of things, but that didn't stop me when I saw what they were at. I went for them.

Michael leaps into action. As he lunges towards the Bailiffs, hundreds of coins fall from his jacket. He struggles with the Bailiffs. Friends including young Tony join him.

We fought for hours, heads were bashed, and I did for about ten of them. But there was too many altogether, so your Ma and me and Lisa locked ourselves into our flat. And wouldn't come out . . .

INT. FLAT, HOLLYFIELD – NIGHT

Michael, Christine, Lisa and Michael's parents barricade themselves into the flat.

MICHAEL

(off)

'You're not taking our home off us no matter what,' we said. And they couldn't get in no matter how hard they tried. They huffed and they puffed, but it was no use. They were rightly fucked off, I'm telling you. And all we could hear around us was the screaming and wailing of our friends and neighbours as they tore their houses into little pieces – like savages, they were.

Bathroom fittings are ripped out, windows are smashed, furniture thrown from great heights. Wholesale and wanton destruction.

And every time we peeked out the window all we could see was our friends and neighbours being driven out of Hollyfield – never to return.

EXT. HOLLYFIELD – NIGHT

Michael's POV of the Bailiffs ruthlessly driving women and children out of their homes.

INT. BOYS' BEDROOM – NIGHT

Michael is utterly lost in his story.

MICHAEL

But they couldn't get us out. They tried everything. They didn't know me. I wouldn't budge. No matter if they brought the whole place down around our ears.

TOMMY

And then the Mayor came.

MICHAEL

That's right – they were so pissed off that they couldn't get the better of me, the Lord Mayor of Dublin himself come out to see your Da . . .

EXT. HOLLYFIELD – DAY

Hollyfield in ruins except for one flat, impossibly intact amid the devastation. Michael, peering through the barricade, sees a fleet of amazing cars arrive. The Lord Mayor steps out in full chains and robe, surrounded by lackeys. One of them is the Judge, now in full dress outfit. Michael steps out of his flat. It is a moment charged with significance as the two meet. The Lord Mayor kneels before Michael and pleads with him.

MICHAEL
(off)

He begged me to leave. He said he was sorry for the way our family had been treated and finally he said to make up for all we had suffered we could have two big houses to live in. One for us and one for Auntie Lisa . . .

The Mayor holds up two golden keys. He looks at Judge forcing him to kneel too. Then Michael graciously accepts the keys.

And I made him promise that no one could ever take our home away from us again. And the Mayor said, 'Yes. I promise.'

The Lord Mayor mouths the words in sync with Michael.

. . . So I graciously accepted their offer.

INT. BOYS' BEDROOM – NIGHT

Michael is so lost that he hasn't noticed the boys are asleep.

MICHAEL

(softly)

I won. I beat them all, boys, the bailiffs and the Mayor, and the Law. I was loyal and that's why I won. You see, the thing is they'll never beat you if you stick together and stay loyal.

Michael looks at the sleeping boys. Smiles and softly kisses them.

EXT. MICHAEL'S HOUSE – NIGHT

Michael throws his leg over the bicycle. He cycles off waving back at Christine framed in the doorway.

CHRISTINE

Night, love – see you tomorrow.

MICHAEL

Night.

EXT. LISA'S HOUSE – NIGHT

Michael arrives at Lisa's house on his bike. Takes out a key, opens the door and wheels the bike in.

INT. LISA'S BEDROOM – NIGHT

Lisa is just a mound in the bed as Michael slips in. He begins to undress.

MICHAEL

Sorry I'm late. Watching telly with Christine. Your man Jerry Springer.

LISA

Oh, you'll have a horn on you so I suppose?

Lisa turns to him and they kiss.

MICHAEL

Any minute now. Oh yeah, what was it I had to tell you? Christine said she forgot to ask you earlier. Will you mind Tommy and Shane tomorrow afternoon, she has to go into town to get Breda her First Communion gear?

LISA

No problem.

MICHAEL

Thanks.

They start to make love. Suddenly there is a terrific hammering on the front door. Michael goes to the window to look out.

EXT. LISA'S HOUSE – NIGHT

Michael sees a squad car sitting outside. Several detectives, including Con and Barry, are standing at the front door.

INT. LISA'S BEDROOM – NIGHT

Fuck 'em. Don't answer.

MICHAEL

Nah. Ring Billy. Tell him what's happened, will you?

INT. INTERROGATION ROOM – NIGHT

Michael in a pool of light, silent, as Barry and Con question him.

CON

Where did you stay? Was it Stevie Brady's house?

Tighten into Michael's impassive face.

BARRY

It was Stevie's house all right.

CON

33 St Dympna's Gardens. Stevie and his eight kids.

BARRY

Slept on the floor, did you?

CON

Very uncomfortable.

BARRY

Handy for the bank, though.

CON

Yeah, it was handy for the bank, wasn't it?

BARRY

We know how you worked it. From the bank to the court.

CON

We do, you know.

BARRY

We have witnesses. They saw the switch.

CON

So come on, Lynch. We'll tell you. All you have to say is yes, that's the way it was.

EXT. GOLF COURSE – DAY

Michael sees in his head a slow motion shot of a golf ball putted into a hole as the interrogation continues.

INT. INTERROGATION ROOM – NIGHT

Out of the corner of his eye Michael sees someone else come in to the interrogation room. The light catches him for a moment. Michael recognises him but doesn't bat an eyelid. It is Noel. He sits in the corner and listens.

BARRY

Who was with you at the bank?

CON

It was Stevie. No, did Stevie drive the car?

CON

Stevie drove the car, right; Tony Brady was with you, yeah?

CU – Michael still outwardly impassive, but thinking pleasing thoughts.

BARRY

We have witnesses, Lynch.

EXT. GOLF COURSE – NIGHT

The interrogation continues as a group of men led by Tony tiptoe across the eighteenth green of a golf course. Beautifully synchronized, they raise large metallic objects and drive them into the green.

CON

(off)

You came to court on the motorbike and switched at the last minute. Right?

BARRY

(off)

Fifteen minutes – easy on a bike, Lynch.

INT. INTERROGATION ROOM – NIGHT

Noel still sits silently in the shadows looking bored.

CON

Give us an answer!

BARRY

All right, all right. We'll start all over again. You didn't sleep with either of your 'wives' on Monday night. We know that much—

NOEL

(casually interrupting)

So Michael, if you weren't with the two ugly sisters, don't tell me you were off banging some other old slag?

Pause. Michael actually flicks an eye at him briefly. Then away and nothing. But Noel has got a reaction at least.

INT. GARDA HQ – MORNING

Noel, bored, on the phone as Barry leads Michael into the lobby. Con is on the other phone dealing with more complaints.

NOEL

Well, the order to bring him in came down from yourself, sir, so I thought sooner rather than later, you know . . .

EXT. GOLF COURSE – DAY

Daly on his mobile, on the ruined eighteenth green. It is now full of perfectly-made holes and coloured flags. Life size cut-outs of famous golfers putting (Ballesteros, Nicklaus, etc.) are also stuck into the green.

DALY

Listen, I realise you're not a golfing man, Detective Sergeant, but the Association of Inspectors and Superintendents' annual outing had to be cancelled today.

. . . Decimated green. Angry golfers.

Now, why do you think it had to be cancelled?

INT./EXT. GARDA HQ – MORNING

NOEL

Well I did mention to you, sir, that things like this usually happen when we try to interrogate – Yes, sir . . . No, I'm not saying I told you so . . .

Michael grins, turns towards the exit, and puts on the balaclava. *[*Barry watches. Lisa is driving. Michael looks at the sky, and says to no one in particular:*

MICHAEL

D'you know what – it's a great day for a game of golf.

Lisa opens the car door for him.

LISA

Did you say golf, Michael?

MICHAEL

I did, Lisa.

LISA

Isn't that weird?

MICHAEL

Why so?

* Cut from completed film.

LISA

Just listening to the news there. And they were saying some golf course was attacked and destroyed last night for no reason at all. The Gardai are baffled. Imagine.

MICHAEL

No way. Like you said, weird.

Noel arrives to see them drive off without a backward glance.]

EXT. MICHAEL'S HOUSE – EVENING

A glorious summer sunset in a residential suburb. Neighbours tend their gardens. Tranquil beauty everywhere. The Lynch home is in stark contrast to the others. The walls are grubby, paint peeling off the doors and windows (which were painted a terrible colour anyway). The garden is a mess and full of rubbish, but Michael and Tommy seem perfectly at peace kneeling by an upturned bicycle, fixing a puncture.

TOMMY

Why does it keep happening, Da?

MICHAEL

Because you don't watch where you're going. You see, every time you go out on the road there's dangers out there. Bits of glass lying in wait, nails, thumb tacks, potholes. So you have to watch out – watch your every move. 'Cause if you don't, they'll get you.

TOMMY

Who?

MICHAEL

The bits of glass and that. Sooner or later if you're not careful. And then you get a puncture. And then you're fucked.

TOMMY

And then you fix it for me.

MICHAEL

Yeah, I do. Aren't you a clever little shite.

TOMMY

(grins, nods)

Can I put the patch on?

MICHAEL

Yeah but don't wrinkle it. There you go. If a job's worth doing . . .

TOMMY

I can't remember.

MICHAEL

It's worth doing well. Say it now.

TOMMY

It's worth doing well.

MICHAEL

Say it all again, to remember it.

TOMMY

(rattles off)

If a job is worth doing then it's worth doing well.

MICHAEL

That's it. Come on, let's pump this thing up, see have we got you on the road again.

EXT. MICHAEL'S HOUSE – DAY

The birdsong and pastoral elegance of Michael's road is disturbed as a convoy of expensive fast cars come roaring up. The gang are arriving for a meeting. They are not a pretty sight.

As well as Stevie, Tony, Alec and Billy (with a crate of beer), there are unfamiliar faces; Shay Kirby, a new man, ex-IRA, arrogant. Tom Rooney, talks too much, considered fairly harmless by the rest, the kind who becomes the butt of jokes. Some others.

INT. MICHAEL'S HOUSE – DAY

A real buzz around the room. There are plates of sandwiches. Billy is in charge of the bottle opener. He is full of chat. Michael drinks lemonade as usual. Some of the children are also roaming around. Christine is rounding them up. Tony is swinging Breda, Michael's seven-year-old daughter, around.

*[TONY

I hear you're making your Holy Communion, honeybunch. Like my Declan. Remember Declan? He wants to marry you, do you know that?

Breda screams with laughter. Christine takes Breda.

* Cut from completed film.

Stevie is having a quiet word in Michael's ear. He likes doing that.]

STEVIE

Michael, your new fellah, Shay Kirby. It doesn't bother you that he used to be in the IRA?

MICHAEL

Nah. He's out a couple of years.

STEVIE

Bit dodgy though, isn't it? Why are you bringing him in?

Michael sometimes gets tired of Stevie.

MICHAEL

He's the inside man on the job I'm going to tell you about. Look, to allay your fears, while I'm talking I'll make a crack about the Provos. Watch how he reacts.

Stevie doesn't think Michael is taking the point seriously enough, but he lets it pass.

Lisa comes in with a final plate of sandwiches.

LISA

Have you enough there?

MICHAEL

Loads, thanks.

CHRISTINE

Tommy, come on, we're going. Tommy, move it! We'll be late for the trailers. Breda, say goodbye to Daddy.

Breda jumps into Michael's arms. He gives her a big kiss.

MICHAEL

Ah chicken, enjoy yourself now.

CHRISTINE

You have everything you need?

MICHAEL

We're grand. Go on, will you.

CHRISTINE

Right, good luck so.

LISA

Bye, lads.

MICHAEL

See you, girls.

The boys all call various goodbyes.

BILLY

(quietly to Alec)

Two for the price of one, ha?

Alec frowns at him to shut up in case Michael hears. The women depart. Door slams. Michael takes charge.

MICHAEL

All right. Sitting down, lads.

BILLY

(throws cans to various gang members)

OK, here we go, last round.

MICHAEL

Little fellah – shut up.

Billy shuts up, grabs a beer and sits, as does everyone else. The room goes quiet. As Michael speaks we take the opportunity to look at his gang.

Right, first of all you've met Shay Kirby. He'll be joining us on this job.

Nods and hellos to Shay.

Now as you know, I'm going to be a bit occupied in the Four Courts from Monday week.

Laughter.

Should go OK, but you never know. So I thought maybe now was time for a job I've been thinking about for the last few months. One of those impossible ones, you know. About two million quid's worth. Now this is one the 'RA had their piggy little eyes on, but even they thought it couldn't be done. Well lads, once I heard that I thought, we're goin' to have to show those dozy fuckers a thing or two about robbin', yeah . . .

General chuckle. Stevie looks at Shay who is chuckling merrily. Maybe it's all right.

O'Donnell's Jewellery factory.

BILLY

Fuck me.

TONY

A-1!

ALEC

Yes!

MICHAEL

So ye're not interested.

General laughter and ad libs.

OK, grab yourselves a sanger while I tell you how it's going to happen.

Munching of sandwiches as the boys settle back like an attentive class.

In the following sequence we feel the source of Michael's power. Even his outlining of the plan has a compelling fairy-tale quality. The sequence of accompanying shots and scenes all feels like a bit of a lark, full of ease and pleasure. The robbery goes like a dream.

It is in fact as if Michael dreamed it, and it happened.

Imagine this lads; in a week or so we're going to be standing somewhere looking at mounds of sparkling jewels and gleaming gold bars. Even after the fences screw us we should each be fifty thousand quid richer. Got it? But first things first. Details. Now O'Donnell's think they have it all figured out . . .

EXT. O'DONNELL'S FACTORY – NIGHT

The wall of O'Donnell's.

MICHAEL

(off)

Very secure high wall – sensor alarms all along the top – touch it anywhere and you're fucked.

The main door and the small entrance door.

Corporation flats. Shots of faces in windows . . .

All the doors fully alarmed. In fact a lot of hassle just getting past the outside wall. Apart from all the locals in the flats next door watching everything that goes on – well, usually.

. . . Then curtains hastily closing as locals see no evil. Michael appears in foreground of shot.

He leads the gang up the flats tower. Over the following dialogue they ready themselves and abseil gracefully over the wall.

And then even if you do get past the wall, the alarm system for the main building is connected to a Garda station not 500 yards away. So there's no point in even trying to break in . . . well, it seems that way. But what I was thinking was . . . we wouldn't try to break into the factory itself, but we would drop in during the night. What you might call a flying visit.

EXT. O'DONNELL'S FACTORY GROUNDS – NIGHT

Michael and some others land in the yard. Michael takes something out of a back pack. The gang begin to work. We don't know what they are doing.

MICHAEL

(off)

Then just sort of . . . I don't know, camp out in the yard until someone arrives to let us in the next morning.

EXT. SMALL DOOR, O'DONNELL'S – DAY

Pompous Fintan Doorley keys in his code to open the small door and enters, the door closing automatically after him.

MICHAEL

(off)

and that someone is . . . Mr Fintan Doorley, the general manager. Like myself he's a very precise man. Fintan arrives at five to eight every morning.

EXT. O'DONNELL'S FACTORY YARD – DAY

Mr Doorley rounds a corner to see . . .

MICHAEL

(off)

Now a man who likes and needs routine, he will probably be a bit surprised at what he sees.

. . . a large brightly coloured tent. He stops in shock; he doesn't know what to make of it. Then Michael and Shay, armed, casually step out to greet him.

And if the shock of that doesn't send poor Fintan's pacemaker out of control – yeah, the old ticker isn't the best – well I'll have to think of something else that will.

Michael takes out a large magnet as Shay grabs hold of Mr Doorley. Michael starts to open his shirt. Mr Doorley looks very ill.

Hopefully this will persuade Mr Doorley that it really is in his own interest to let us inside.

Mr Doorley produces keys. Michael and Shay lead him to the main building.

INT. DOORLEY'S OFFICE – DAY

Shay sits at a desk and turns on a monitor. On screen is the area outside the small door.

MICHAEL

(off)

So while Fintan and myself investigate the strong room, Shay will do what Mr Doorley normally does every morning – monitor the arrival of his twenty-five staff . . .

EXT. SMALL DOOR, O'DONNELL'S – DAY

Staff arrive in twos and threes. They buzz and look up at the camera.

INT. DOORLEY'S OFFICE – DAY

Shay presses a button to let them in.

MICHAEL

(off)

. . . and believe me, none of them want to be late for Mr Doorley. Once inside they will meet Tony, Tom and Billy who will invite them into the marquee . . .

EXT. O'DONNELL'S FACTORY YARD – DAY

The staff members turn the corner just like Mr Doorley and encounter the tent and the smiling faces of Tony, Tom and Billy who usher them into the tent.

INT. DOORLEY'S OFFICE – DAY

Cutting between Shay in the office looking at the monitor.

EXT. SMALL DOOR, O'DONNELL'S – DAY

More staff members arriving at the small door.

EXT. O'DONNELL'S FACTORY YARD – DAY

Staff members grabbed by Billy, Tom and Tony and being bound and gagged inside the tent.

MICHAEL

(off)

And lads – politely, OK. As long as they're doing us no harm, we won't do them any harm.

Billy is showing off – rougher than he needs to be.

You got that, Billy?

BILLY

(off)

Hm? Oh yeah, sure.

Billy suddenly seems to remember and stops hassling the staff.

MICHAEL

(off)

Once all the staff have arrived and the strong room is opened, Shay will let Alec in and we give ourselves no more than ten minutes to load up . . .

EXT. O'DONNELL'S GATES – DAY

The main doors open and Alec drives in.

EXT. O'DONNELL'S FACTORY YARD – DAY

Bulging coalsacks are passed hand to hand.

The gang march cheerily with coalsacks full of loot and toss them into the van.

Michael, orchestrating, is now on his Kawasaki.

Hiace doors and car boots are slammed. The gang jump back into their vehicles.

MICHAEL

(off)

. . . so that by quarter to nine, we all drive back out again. And we can relax 'cause it should be some time before anyone gets to contact the Gardai.

The staff are bound and gagged in the tent.

INT. DOORLEY'S OFFICE – DAY

Doorley is bound and gagged in his office.

EXT. O'DONNELL'S FACTORY YARD – DAY

Michael's convoy eases out into the morning traffic.

MICHAEL

(off)

Then it's only a matter of waiting a few days to sort out the haul, until we all meet up for the split.

INT. MICHAEL'S HOUSE – DAY

Back in the living-room the gang are enthralled. Michael smiles benignly, pouring himself another lemonade.

MICHAEL

Now does everyone have a picture of that in their heads, because lads, I promise you, that's just the way it's going to be – easy as pie.

INT. PIGEON HOUSE – NIGHT

In pools of light on snooker tables there are mounds of jewels surrounded by bundles of gold bars, all divided equally. The gang drink in the beauty of the scene.

STEVIE

(to Alec)

What are you, eight, ten years younger than me and Billy say, right? Big difference. And then Tony and Michael add another ten years on to that. They had fuck all. Isn't that right Michael, when you were kids?

MICHAEL

We had each other. OK, it's all yours, lads. One pile each. Take your pick, they're all equal.

Stevie and Alec talk as they bag their loot.

STEVIE

Now, I'm that much younger, so I got some stuff as a kid, but it was never the right stuff.

ALEC

What are you shitin' on about?

STEVIE

Billy knows what I'm talkin' about, don't you?

BILLY

No.

STEVIE

Ah fuck. What was the big thing when you were . . . eight, say?

ALEC

Ah – Star Wars, I suppose. Is that what you mean?

STEVIE

Exactly. Now I bet you got the proper Star Wars stuff. The real toys. What were they called?

ALEC

The Luke Skywalker doll, Darth Vader . . . sure, yeah.

STEVIE

And it was the proper thing? You know, the official stuff.

ALEC

Yeah – so.

STEVIE

Well I never got that – the real thing.

ALEC

But, sure, me da probably robbed it.

STEVIE

Doesn't matter. My ma and da couldn't even rob the proper thing. Like Scalextrix – that was like, the dream, when I was a kid.

BILLY

Yeah, that's right – and Subbutteo.

STEVIE

Fuck Subbutteo. Scalextrix is what we're talkin' about. It was the name. The ad on the telly. What did I get? Some Mickey Mouse other racing car thing, some cheap imitation that was supposed to be like it. But it was nothing like it. And Meccano. Did you ever hear of that? I never had the real Meccano set. I had some other . . . crap!

ALEC

That's a tragedy, Stevie.

STEVIE

It is yeah, that's what I'm saying. And bad timing. Tony and Michael never had anything except suckie sweets. Me and Billy had stuff but it was some crap cheap version of the thing I really wanted. Fellahs your age got thc proper thing, and now my kids expect every fuckin' thing that's going.

ALEC

And you're going to use all your dosh, to make sure they get it.

STEVIE

In my hole. I'm going to make up for all the stuff I missed out on. I'm going to enjoy myself. Hey, Michael!

MICHAEL

Yeah.

STEVIE

I have to say it, man. Fair dues to you.

MICHAEL

And you Stevie.

All the gang agree. They whoop and cheer and rattle their jewellery. Michael grins. He seems very contented.

FADE TO BLACK

INT. PIGEON HOUSE – NIGHT

Michael looks down from his office as Tom rehearses his story by the car.

INT. PIGEON HOUSE – NIGHT

The boot of Tom's car closes on a pile of gold bars. Tom explains at unnecessary length how the gold will be transported. He opens the driver's door.

TOM

You see, the depth of the door is just right. Now you see once these panels are removed the bars sit in there, ah! Nice and snug. If you have enough of them they don't rattle around, and you don't even notice the extra weight when you're opening and closing the door.

MICHAEL

OK. I get it, Tom.

TOM

Now this couple I've lined up are complete innocents – that's the beauty of it – no extra splits. They're just old friends of me da's going to England on their holidays; a couple in their fifties, Mr and Mrs Harmless. And you know Customs . . .

EXT. FERRYPORT, HOLYHEAD – DAY

TOM

(off)

. . . While they're busy searching bearded ex-hippies in 2CVs, they'll be tipping their hats at our pair as they chugga chugga through at their usual twenty-five mile an hour . . .

British Customs Men are indeed tipping their caps to the Old Couple, while in the background a Bearded Radical with partner and free range child have their car taken apart.

Tom babbles on over the next action.

EXT. COUNTRY ROAD – DAY

TOM

(off)

Then they'll drive all the way over to the Cotswolds. They've told me all about the lovely hotel that's so quiet and peaceful that they always go back every year . . .

The couple scrutinise a map as they drive. They are lost. He pulls the car in. They seem to disagree on directions. Impatient, he opens his door without checking behind.

A Land Rover flies by, taking the driver's door with it.

The horrified couple look at their door lying on the road. They go to it. To their shock, they cannot lift it.

TOM

(off)

. . . This is how I see it all happening. It's not too far from Birmingham so I can fly in, be at their hotel in half an hour. They'll be there taking afternoon tea, completely unaware that they've got a couple of hundred thousand quid's worth of gold sitting outside in their car . . .

Having checked the damage to their Land Rover, two muscular men come back to the Couple. They help lift the door, but to everyone's bemusement, all four together cannot do it.

INT. PIGEON HOUSE – NIGHT

TOM

. . . And the kind of hotel it is, there'll be no more than a dozen cars parked there. No security, so getting at the car will be no problem. Bing bang boom! Get the gold. Bring it to the fence—

MICHAEL

Yeah, fine Tom. It all sounds fine. I'll see you when you get back, so.

EXT. HOTEL GROUNDS – DAY

Michael, Christine, Lisa and all the children are dressed up. Breda is wearing an extravagant communion dress.

BREDA

Granny! Granny!

Michael's parents, Padraig and Mona, embrace their grandchild on her special day. General excitement and squealing as everyone mills around.

*[MONA

Christine – there is no need for all this. I had sandwiches made back at the house.

CHRISTINE

Michael wanted you to have a day out too.

MONA

But these old restaurants are very dear. And you're waiting ages to get served.

CHRISTINE

Mam! Enjoy yourself.]

Breda runs over to Michael clutching an embossed book.

BREDA

Da, Da, look what Granny gave me.

* Cut from completed film.

MICHAEL

What is it, chicken?

BREDA

A holy book with a gold cover, and coloured pictures.

Michael looks at the book: 'My First Holy Communion Book'.

MICHAEL

Oh, brilliant, what I'd give to get a present like that.

A neighbour waves.

*[Look, there's Mrs Cassidy. Go on over, I think she might have something for you. I'll mind your book for you.]

Breda runs to get a big hug and a kiss from Mrs Cassidy, who also slips something into Breda's hand.

*[*Michael watches this as he takes some £20 notes from his pocket, folds them and slides them into Breda's book. The page he opens has a luridly mournful illustration of the crucifixion.*] *As he does this he notices a car arriving and Billy getting out. Billy seems nervous. He speaks to the man inside the car who indicates Breda. Billy turns and calls her. Breda runs to them. The man smiles and gives her money. Padraig joins Michael.*

MICHAEL

Da, who's he again? Should I know him?

* Cut from completed film.

PADRAIG

I dunno – it's funny, he looks more like you than your brother does. Same hairdo an' all.

MICHAEL

Why do I feel like I should know him?

PADRAIG

Oh, hold on, I have him now. He grew up around our way all right. Went to college an' all after – Higgins is his name.

(drops his voice)

IRA, I heard.

Breda returns delighted, brandishing money.

BREDA

Look what I got, Da.

MICHAEL

(passing the prayer book)

Lucky old you. Here you go. Mind that now, it's very precious.

Michael sees Higgins squeeze Billy's arm before driving off.

Come on, Dad – Tony and his crowd will be waiting with their tongues hanging out.

INT. HOTEL – DAY

Michael and Tony walk together. Tony seems nervous.

TONY

Ah . . . Michael . . . you know that thing Tom was ah . . . doing for you in England?

Michael immediately smells trouble.

MICHAEL

Go on.

TONY

Well, you see . . . that's it, you see . . . Michael, I always thought that even though Tom was a bit of a fucking eejit, he was sound you know. Like if you asked me, that's what I would have told you.

They reach the restaurant door. Michael looks at him.

It looks like . . . he's done a runner.

MICHAEL

(casual)

Yeah?

As he goes into the restaurant, Michael stiffens. He sees Noel outside standing by the door of the toilets. He is not looking in Michael's direction.

INT. HOTEL – DAY

Michael and Tony move through a sea of communion dresses and suits.

MICHAEL

Why the fuck would he think he could get away with it?

TONY

It's not like him, I'll say that for him. I don't know like, can you ever trust anyone?

Michael is still staring at Noel. Is Noel following him? Noel, still not looking, seems very casual.

MICHAEL

Yeah, you do. That's what it's all about. I wouldn't have let him do the job if I didn't trust him.

TONY

Yeah, but what now?

MICHAEL

Go find him. Bring him back.

Tony walks off immediately.

Tony – you can eat your dinner first.

Tony grins and goes back to the table. Michael turns again to where Noel is. A woman and twins, both in communion dress, now come out of the ladies toilet. They join Noel who smiles at them. His wife and daughters. It's his communion day too. Michael grins, relaxes.

*[BREDA

(running up)

Do you know how much I've made now, Da?

* Cut from completed film.

MICHAEL

No matter how much it is – you're worth it, honeybunch.]

As he looks at Noel leaving the hotel with his wife and daughters, Michael hunkers down to Breda and hugs her.

EXT. MERRION SQUARE – DAY

Michael, with Christine as passenger on the Kawasaki, rides up to the entrance gates of the National Art Gallery. A huge banner proclaims the Caravaggio exhibition. A large queue waits. Christine hops off.

MICHAEL

Jesus, are you going to queue up?

CHRISTINE

I'll have to, won't I? Unless you've any better ideas.

MICHAEL

I could get you in no bother. A private tour.

CHRISTINE

Ah, no thanks. I'll try the front door.

MICHAEL

Fair enough. Listen, I'd better move. I've this stupid fuckin' court thing in half an hour. Enjoy yourself.

CHRISTINE

I will. Listen – you'll be all right will you?

Michael just grins under the balaclava and rides off.

INT. COURT – DAY

Michael seems ill at ease, wearing a suit in the crowded stuffy court. Harrison rises to speak.

HARRISON

Your honour, may I make an application to adjourn proceedings until Wednesday—

JUDGE

Application denied.

HARRISON

But your honour—

JUDGE

Mr Harrison, the prosecution is ready, the jury is ready, I am ready. Your client cannot avoid the process of law indefinitely. Mr McHale, are you ready to begin?

Harrison looks at Michael. He now knows exactly what to expect from this Judge. Michael sees Noel smile slightly.

McHALE

(rather pleased)

Certainly, your honour. Good morning, ladies and gentlemen. Almost two years ago on the 19th of February 1990, the defendant, Michael Lynch and an unknown associate, entered the offices of Superex, a video game company. They were armed and dangerous. They threatened the life of a member of staff and they stole over £32,000 in cash . . .

INT. MICHAEL'S HOUSE – EVENING

CHRISTINE

Listen, Michael, d'you see this.

Christine holds up a poster of Caravaggio's 'The Taking of Christ' from the National Art Gallery.

Do you mind if I hang it up in our room?

MICHAEL

A holy picture. What do you want a holy picture for?

CHRISTINE

I knew you'd say that. It's not a holy picture. It's a Caravaggio. He was about as holy as you are.

MICHAEL

Looks like a holy picture to me.

CHRISTINE

Can I hang it up or can't I?

MICHAEL

Of course you can.

CHRISTINE

And you won't be slagging me about it?

MICHAEL

I promise.

CHRISTINE

Grand.

She goes. Michael winks at Tommy.

MICHAEL

Women, ha?

INT. PIGEON HOUSE – NIGHT

CU – *a car door is slammed on a hand. Excruciating scream of pain.*

Michael, sitting inside the car, has slammed the door on Tom's hand. Stevie and Tony hold on to Tom outside.

MICHAEL

I don't know; do you get the feeling, Tom, that I don't believe you.

TOM

Please Michael, please, I swear.

Michael cocks an ear and rolls down the car window.

MICHAEL

I mean, even if it is true that these aul' ones got their car door ripped off by a passing Land Rover and left it abandoned on the side of the motorway . . .

TOM

I searched, Michael – I drove up and down.

MICHAEL

Hold on to him there, lads – but you see, you didn't come back to tell me this straight away.

Michael opens the car door suddenly and violently. Tom is bashed by it even as he is released, and squeals pathetically.

TOM

I was afraid. I'd fucked up and I was afraid.

MICHAEL

You don't think I'm a fair man then, Tom.

TOM

No Michael, it's not that – oh Jesus, Michael. I'm . . . sorry. Please, please.

Michael looks up as a large hook drops down towards them.

MICHAEL

What did you do with the gold?

TOM

Oh God. Oh God. Nothing. I did nothing.

Michael attaches Tom's good arm to the hook.

I never got it. I never. It – it's gone. You have to believe me, I—

Michael signals to Stevie who sets the machinery in motion, pulling the hook with Tom attached, jerking him into the air. Tom screams. As he is pulled along in mid air, Michael follows him.

MICHAEL

You ran away, Tom. Only scumbags run away. You can't trust someone who does that. Would you trust them, Tom? Would you?

TOM

N-n-no.

MICHAEL

So you see why this is a problem we have to deal with, don't you? I can't be hanging around, Tom.

TOM

Yes . . .

MICHAEL

So where's the gold!

TOM

(screams)

I don't knooooWWW!!

Leaving Tom hanging there whimpering, Michael motions to Tony and Stevie. He speaks quietly.

LZG·99

MICHAEL

What do you think?

Stevie and Tony are reluctant to air any firm opinion.

STEVIE

I don't know, Michael.

TONY

I'd say – I mean . . . not certain or anything, now. But I'd nearly believe him.

MICHAEL

(casually)

Yeah, I think you're right. His story is so stupid it's probably true. OK, get him down.

He turns back to Tom.

I was wrong about you, Tom. I believe your story now. Tony will take you to the hospital. Are you on the medical card, by the way – I mean this won't cost you anything, will it?

Tom cannot speak. But he nods his head and moans an assent.

Grand so. 'Night.

INT. COURT – DAY

The trial continues. Noel is in the stand. Michael has his head bowed throughout, showing no interest.

McHALE

And based on the evidence you had gathered, you concluded that it was a Michael Lynch operation.

NOEL

Absolutely. You see, the accused is a very clever man.

HARRISON

Objection, your honour, this is opinion not evidence.

JUDGE

Overruled.

HARRISON

If I may respectfully—

JUDGE

Detective Sergeant Quigley as an experienced police officer is entitled to draw conclusions from his investigations. And the jury may decide if they are fair and reasonable. That is up to them. Go on, Detective Sergeant, you were about to explain to us exactly what a Michael Lynch operation is – And will the accused sit up and let us see his face, please!

Michael is forced to sit up. He looks directly and coldly at the Judge. It is frightening.

NOEL

The accused is a genuinely clever man. Exceptionally so. But ah . . . the odd thing is he can't help letting people know how clever he is. Sometimes I think he's not really a proper criminal, even – he's just a big show-off.

As Harrison objects again, Noel looks at Michael with a 'you're fucked, Lynch' smirk.

INT. BAR – DAY

Michael joins Shay at the bar.

MICHAEL

What'll it be?

SHAY

(a little nervy)

I'm grand – Everything go all right with Tom?

Michael's mind is completely on something else as he passes a piece of paper to Shay.

MICHAEL

Hm? Ah yeah, fine – this fuckin' Judge is getting on my nerves. He's, ah – he's prejudiced, you know.

SHAY

Yeah?

MICHAEL

(referring to piece of paper)

That's his daughter's car.

SHAY

Yeah?

MICHAEL

Mmmm. The trial will be over by Thursday – does that give you enough time?

SHAY

Ah – ah – OK.

Michael smiles at him.

EXT. JUDGE'S HOME – EVENING

The Judge opens his front door saying goodnight to his Daughter and her Boyfriend. It is raining.

BOYFRIEND

Give me the keys, love. Thanks again, sir, for a very stimulating evening.

The Boyfriend shakes hands, takes the car keys and dashes off into the rainy night. Judge kisses his Daughter.

DAUGHTER

Hope we didn't outstay our welcome, Dad.

JUDGE

Not at all. Mind you, he does like the sound of his own voice, doesn't he?

DAUGHTER

You're the one to talk. You're just annoyed that there's actually someone who dares to argue back—

An explosion. Judge and Daughter, shocked, turn to hear Boyfriend's car blowing up. Daughter screams hysterically and tries to run towards the scene of the explosion. Judge holds her back.

INT. FOUR COURTS – DAY

A deadly tense courtroom silence. Noel is tight with rage. Michael stares calmly smiling at the Judge who is staring into space. Lost. Frightened.

JUDGE

Ah . . . in conclusion, whatever the Jury's feelings may be as to what seems the most just conclusion to draw, I must remind you that you are compelled to abide by the strict requirements of evidence. If the available evidence is not sufficient for a conviction, then . . . you must not convict . . .

EXT. FOUR COURTS – DAY

Michael emerges to a scrum of photographers and a barrage of questions.

JOURNALIST 1

You're found not guilty, Michael – can't we see your face now?

JOURNALIST 2

Mr Lynch – any comment to make on rumours of intimidation?

JOURNALIST 3

Give us a wave, Michael.

JOURNALIST 4

Mr Lynch, 98 FM. Can you reassure the people of Dublin that you are no threat to their safety?

JOURNALIST 5

What do you think of the Gardai now, Michael?

JOURNALIST 6

Do you think the criminal justice system is too soft on criminals, Michael?

JOURNALIST 7

How can you afford such an expensive legal team, Mr Lynch?

JOURNALIST 8

Are you back on the dole now, Michael?

JOURNALIST 9

Take off the hood just for a sec, would you? One smile.

Michael grins under his balaclava and waves at the photographers. He spots Noel in the distance and gives him the thumbs up. Noel turns away in disgust.

EXT. FOUR COURTS – DAY

Noel is interviewed by journalists.

JOURNALIST

This is another disaster for the Gardai, isn't it?

NOEL

We'd certainly have preferred a different result.

JOURNALIST

But you accept that Mr Lynch is innocent.

NOEL

I accept that he has had a fair trial and been found not guilty. That is not to say there is not more to find out about him. And the Gardai intend to find out.

JOURNALIST

But the more you hound him the more ordinary people seem to think he's a great laugh.

NOEL

I think events have now shown that Michael Lynch's jokes just aren't very funny. He thinks he can have a laugh at the whole country's expense. Well not any more.

JOURNALIST

But it does seem like the Gardai just can't cope with the spiral of crime in the city right now.

NOEL

Well we just have to find ways to cope.

*[EXT. FOUR COURTS – DAY

Christine and Lisa drive up to steps of Four Courts.]

INT. MICHAEL'S HOUSE – EVENING

Michael, Christine and Lisa sit together on the couch. The kids are gathered round sprawling on the floor. They are all watching

* Cut from completed film.

the video of the news report on Michael's release. They cheer as Michael comes down the steps through the crowd and gets into the car. There is a shot of Noel being interviewed.

NOEL
(on TV)
I think events have now shown that Michael Lynch's jokes just aren't very funny. He thinks he can have a laugh at the whole country's expense. Well not any more.

Michael freezes it instantly.

MICHAEL
D'you see him lads. You know what he is, don't you?

TOMMY
Is he a pig, Da?

MICHAEL
That's right. But never say pig. Always say Garda. And never trust him, or anyone like him, OK.

CHRISTINE
Ah come on, play it, Michael. Are me or Lisa in it at all?

MICHAEL
A small bit, you have to really watch out for it.

They watch closely. Michael freezes the shot again. It is just about possible to make out Lisa and Christine in the car as it whizzes past.

LISA

Yeah, that's us. We're famous.

CHRISTINE

We're not the stars of the show, of course. We'd only be like extras, you know.

*[LISA

Well as soon as Michael is finished admiring himself, I've a bit of news for you.

CHRISTINE

What?

LISA

Not 'til he turns that off. Lads, come on. Play outside.

Chorus of groans.

Michael, turn it off. Out, I said, go on.

The kids all go. The TV is turned off. Christine and Michael look at Lisa, who sits down between them, enjoying the drama.

CHRISTINE

So . . . come on, tell us.

LISA

Well. I'm pregnant again.

Christine and Michael are delighted.

* Cut from completed film.

CHRISTINE

Oh, brilliant. Congratulations.

MICHAEL

Heyyy – my girl. Fuck me, ha?

CHRISTINE

When did you hear?

LISA

To be honest I found out for sure about a week ago.

CHRISTINE

What?

LISA

But I thought, better say nothing 'til after the trial, you know.

CHRISTINE

Ahh. Well sure, now we've two reasons to celebrate.

MICHAEL

Right girls, where'll we go?]

EXT. STREET – NIGHT

Rain pours down but Michael, Lisa and Christine don't care as they fall out of the chipper arm in arm. They raucously sing 'You Left Me Just When I Needed You Most'. *Not exactly close harmony, but great fun as they turn up their own road.*

CHRISTINE/MICHAEL/LISA

Now I need you more
than I did before
and how I'll find comfort, God only knows!
But youuuuuuuuuuuu . . . left me
just when I needed you most
But youuuuuu . . . left me
just when I needed you most.

An electric car window opens as they pass. A voice speaks.

HIGGINS

(off)

That's very nice. Night – Lisa and Christine, isn't it? Sorry, I'm not sure which is which. Dark, you know.

MICHAEL

Who's that?

Billy steps out of the car.

BILLY

Michael, how're you. It's Jerome Higgins. He wants to talk to you.

MICHAEL

Jerome Higgins? Since when have you become a messenger boy for the IRA, little fellah?

HIGGINS

(off)

We've done a few favours for Billy.

Michael looks at Billy's worn-out hunted eyes and understands.

BILLY

Talk to him, will you. A few minutes. Honestly, it's not trouble or anything . . . what's the problem?

MICHAEL

I don't like being told what to do – that's the problem.

BILLY

Don't I know. Please, Michael. Ha?

Billy sounds in trouble. Michael looks at Christine. Her look says 'talk to him'. He shrugs.

MICHAEL

I won't be long, OK.

CHRISTINE

Grand.

The girls walk on. Michael walks to the car. Higgins speaks from inside it.

HIGGINS

Glad our man Shay Kirby was able to be of help to you with that judge, Michael.

MICHAEL

Shay isn't in the IRA any—

HIGGINS

Ah, but his training, Michael. His methods, Here, sit in.

MICHAEL

What are you looking for?

Michael stays in the rain, looking in the back door.

HIGGINS

I was saying to Billy there that I think there could be a lot of merit in a bit of co-operation between us.

MICHAEL

Well I don't.

HIGGINS

Billy wouldn't agree with you. Now I suppose you know we had our eye on O'Donnell's Jewellery as well.

MICHAEL

Tough shit.

HIGGINS

So a reasonable cut from the . . . what? two million I believe, would be a nice gesture to us, Michael. Call it – a symbol of future collaboration.

MICHAEL

A symbol of future fuck all. You haven't neither the fucking brains or the gumption to do your own robbin', so you think you can squeeze an ordinary decent criminal who knows something about his job.

Michael turns away.

Fuck off and double fuck off, Jerome.

He looks at Billy, who looks completely ashamed.

Good night, little fellah.

He walks over to the women. He looks back, grinning.

No hard feelings, by the way. God loves a tryer. And keep an eye on the newspapers, Higgins 'cause that'll be the first time you'll hear about my next job, when it's all over the front pages. The biggest yet, way out of your league.

Christine is waiting anxiously.

CHRISTINE

What job are you talking about?

MICHAEL

Don't ask me. I was making it up as I went along. The fucker.

EXT. MICHAEL'S HOUSE – NIGHT

Billy stands in the rain, knocking on the door.

BILLY

Michael, Michael, it's me.

INT. MICHAEL'S HOUSE – NIGHT

Michael opens the door. Billy stands forlorn in the rain. What can he say?

MICHAEL

Get us a couple of ton out of the box, Christine. So . . . you were dealing and got yourself in hock to the IRA. Fuckin' spa. I want you gone out of Dublin fast, little fellah. England, the States, wherever. But keep away from them and keep away from me, OK?

Billy nods. Christine returns with cash. Michael hands it to Billy and just closes the door in his rain-soaked face.

INT. MICHAEL'S BEDROOM – NIGHT

Michael and Christine are in bed. Both are asleep but Michael is restless. He wakes up suddenly. He looks at the poster of The Taking of Christ that Christine had pinned on the wall. Suddenly it hits him. He leans over and kisses Christine, delighted. She moves, half-awake.

*[CHRISTINE

Ah Michael, stop.

MICHAEL

Hey Christine, Christine . . . will you do me a big favour?

CHRISTINE

I'm too tired, love . . .

MICHAEL

Don't worry, tomorrow will do fine.]

EXT. NATIONAL GALLERY – DAY

* Cut from completed film.

Michael and Christine stand in a long queue of people outside the National Gallery. There is a big canopy over the main door announcing the Caravaggio exhibition.

CHRISTINE

Mostly he ended up doing religious paintings but that was only 'cause that's where the money was in those days. Cardinals and bishops were always hiring artists to paint scenes from the Bible. And lords of course, trying to show off how holy they were . . .

Michael notes video cameras at each end of the building.

INT. NATIONAL GALLERY – DAY

Michael and Christine walk along the corridor.

Caravaggio had to do a runner out of Rome after he killed some fellah in a fight. A bit of a headcase, you know . . .

Again Michael notes the video cameras, the narrowness of the corridor, and the ushers positioned at entrances.

INT. NATIONAL GALLERY – DAY

Michael and Christine arrive at the dimly lit room where The Taking of Christ is housed.

CHRISTINE

You see Jesus and Judas . . . he just used fellahs off the street as his models. He hung around bars and whorehouses all the time, and he'd pick out someone that looked interesting to be Jesus or whoever. I think he got a kick out of that, you know, having Cardinals on their knees, praying away to some painting of a murderer or something.

As Christine talks Michael looks closely at the painting. In his mind's eye the face of Christ turns into his own face. Judas becomes Higgins.

Michael grins at his little fantasy.

What are you laughing at?

MICHAEL

Oh, nothing. I was just thinking you know, about what lasts, and who gets the benefit. I mean your man who painted this – who did all the work, never got the money. Just gets himself run out of town and bumped off. He gets the reputation all right, and we all think he's great and so on, but he never saw any of that money it's supposed to be worth, did he? I mean like – what's the fucking point then, right?

CHRISTINE

Are you afraid no one will remember you after you're dead? I think you should take up painting.

MICHAEL

What, so I'll be remembered?

CHRISTINE

No, so you can do the kitchen.

EXT. JESUIT COMMUNITY HOUSE – DAY

The door of a Georgian townhouse opens and a young priest in civvies, Grogan, smiles at Christine and Michael who smile back.

FATHER GROGAN

Hello, yes?

CHRISTINE

Father Grogan?

FATHER GROGAN

Paul Grogan, yes that's me.

CHRISTINE

My name is Christine. I phoned you about the Caravaggio.

FATHER GROGAN

Of course, come in. Welcome.

They all go inside.

INT. JESUIT COMMUNITY HOUSE – DAY

Father Grogan brings Michael and Christine into the basement refectory. As Father Grogan talks on, Michael sizes up the room, especially the window leading to the back yard.

FATHER GROGAN

It was hanging right there for years, looking down at everyone eating their supper and no one took any notice of it. Getting dirtier and dirtier. Then one day I was celebrating mass in our little chapel upstairs – remind me to show it to you before you go – anyway, that morning it was Luke's wonderfully moving account of Veronica washing the face of Jesus. I thought, we must have that beautiful painting cleaned. No idea what was about to be uncovered: a Caravaggio, a priceless original. It was a pity for us of course in a way, because it was lovely to have it there. But well, as soon as we knew its value, we all realised it couldn't stay here. I mean any half-decent thief could just walk in, although it hasn't happened so far, touch wood. The gallery made us that very fine copy though.

He points to the painting at the other end of the room. It is indeed a fine version of The Taking of Christ. Michael looks closely.

MICHAEL

Same size and all, yeah?

FATHER GROGAN

Oh yes. An absolute replica. I couldn't tell the difference.

CHRISTINE

I couldn't either.

MICHAEL

What about an art expert?

FATHER GROGAN

Ah well. He – or she – would spot it in seconds. There's about half a dozen immediate visual clues. You've probably learned all about them, Christine, for your research.

CHRISTINE

Yes, yes. That's right. I haven't really, you know, started work on that part of it yet—

MICHAEL

And if it's really worth £30 million, why didn't you sell it to the gallery instead of giving it to them?

FATHER GROGAN

Good question. Well, not blowing our own trumpets now, but I suppose we just thought it was the right thing to do.

Michael is impressed.

EXT. NATIONAL GALLERY – DAY

A large minibus emblazoned with the name RAFTERY TOURS and underneath the slogan 'We'll give you the runaround' is parked in a prime spot outside the National Gallery.

What appears to be a group of American Tourists disembark and join the queue. Loud clothes, lots of baseball caps, hats, sunglasses effectively hiding faces. On closer examination it is of course Michael and the gang in simple, if tasteless disguise. Michael turns to the Official Driver.

MICHAEL

(American accent)

I don't think we're gonna do more than ten minutes here, so stand by ready for us, would you pal.

DRIVER

Yeah sure – no problem.

They move as a block into the gallery.

INT. NATIONAL GALLERY – DAY

The gang move with the crowd into the room that houses The Taking of Christ.

They spread out around the room, each watching Michael, closely waiting for the signal. Tony stays by his side as they stand directly in front of The Taking of Christ.

Rather cheekily, Michael turns and takes Tony's face in his hands just as Judas does to Christ in the painting. Immediately all the gang reach into their hats or wherever, and pull their balaclavas on. They move to various other paintings in the room and begin to take them down.

The alarms ring and the Security Voice urgently names the location of the trouble. As the rest of the crowd look on aghast, not quite knowing what is happening, Michael and Tony step forward and remove The Taking of Christ.

The Ushers step forward, but now the rest of the gang hold their various paintings like shields, as they form a protective circle around Michael and Tony. Stevie and Shay produce guns and fire in the air. The crowd scream and back off. The Ushers hesitate and can do nothing as the gang drive at them inside their circle of paintings. The possibility of damaging even the lesser works makes everyone reluctant to do anything.

INT. NATIONAL GALLERY – DAY

The gang rush down the narrow corridor. Alarm bells are still ringing madly. Security Men gather to stop them, but once again the combination of the presence of guns and the danger of destroying the works of art makes them hold back.

The gang move with practised ease in a circle towards the exit. Michael walks casually in the middle of it, like a head of state protected by his secret service. He holds The Taking of Christ carefully by his side. The crowd is in frightened disarray as the gang reach the front door.

EXT. NATIONAL GALLERY – DAY

The inevitable sound of sirens are heard as the gang now break for the minibus, still using the other paintings as a shield held towards the security people who now crowd out the main entrance.

The Driver looks around in shock at the commotion as he is grabbed by Alec and turfed out. Michael and the gang pile in. The minibus pulls away.

The chase begins.

EXT. MERRION SQUARE – DAY

Squad cars now appear as the minibus screams around Merrion Square. Michael goes to the back window and watches intently as two squad cars close in behind the minibus. He nods at Stevie who picks up a painting of a nude and stands waiting.

Michael sees a detective marksman emerge from an open car window with his rifle. As he prepares to fire, Michael opens the back window of the minibus slightly and nods again to Stevie who hangs the painting out, making sure that the detectives see it, before dropping it on to the road in front of them. Instinctively the squad car brakes and swerves to avoid destroying the work of art. The two squad cars collide.

MICHAEL

See that. I knew we were a country that respects art.

*[INT. VAN – HUBBAND BRIDGE AREA – DAY

Inside the van Michael now fits a piece of mirrored glass into the frame, neatly covering the Caravaggio.

EXT. LANE NEAR HUBBAND BRIDGE – DAY

The minibus swings into the lane and stops. All the remaining gang pile out. Before he gets out, Shay sets a small explosive. All except Michael jump into a car. Michael brings The Taking of Christ, now concealed by the mirror, and attaches it to the outside of a small van with the name OLD MASTERS GLAZING COMPANY and the tag-line 'We help you see through everything' on it. He gets in and drives off slowly. He disappears from view as the foreground explosion destroys the minibus.

EXT. CANAL LOCK, HUBBAND BRIDGE – DAY

Michael's van with the framed mirror drives past as Garda cars converge on the lock. Gardai and passers-by are helping Barry and Con from the lock.

* Cut from completed film.

Paintings float in the canal. People fall in as they try to retrieve them.]

INT. PIGEON HOUSE – NIGHT

Music plays. Michael climbs the stairs from the floor of the warehouse to his office. Tony, Stevie, Alec and Tom follow behind him. They drink beer, Michael a lemonade.

MICHAEL

Never mind if there's bastards out there trying to get you, that's only satisfied when they can grind you down, keep you poor, put you away. They don't count. Not with us. In fact I think we can give them the runaround any time we like, 'cause they're only eejits –

The gang murmur in agreement.

– mentioning no names, like. Oh, you know this thing of me becoming a bit of a TV star lately. Well, I want you all to know – it's not goin' to change me one little bit.

Laughter from the boys.

INT. PIGEON HOUSE OFFICE – NIGHT

Michael is in high form as he throws open the door into his darkened office. He waits while they all assemble and closes the door.

MICHAEL

For your eyes only, lads. Wait 'til you see this.

He puts the lights on. One entire wall is covered with The Taking of Christ surrounded by press cuttings. Huge headlines about the robbery. They all whoop and cheer.

INT. PIGEON HOUSE – NIGHT

MICHAEL

Every paper in the country and most of the Brit papers too. And none of them have a fucking clue who did it. Do you want to see the TV thing? I have a tape of it here.

He turns on the TV, which is directly under The Taking of Christ. Shaky handheld shots of Michael leaving court, leaving the Dole Office, hooded. TV crews pursue his car.

The TV, the Caravaggio, the newspaper headlines: the effect is quite surreal.

STEVIE

So how are we getting rid of it, Michael?

MICHAEL

All sussed – Alec is going to Amsterdam next week to check out this fence I've been told about. A specialist. Look, Det-Sergeant Quigley who thought I'd run out of jokes.

NOEL

(on TV)

I think events have shown that Michael Lynch's jokes just aren't that funny. He thinks he can have a laugh at the whole country's expense. Well not any more.

Michael presses his face to the screen.

MICHAEL

Can't I? You've no answers, have you? Don't know what's going on . . . and if this fence is OK we'll bring him back here, show him the stuff, let him make an offer. But the crack is, while we're waiting for all that, we can just sit back and watch the Gardai making a pig's mickey of it.

*[TONY

Can I just say—

(putting his arm around Michael)

Can I just say that this man, this baldy bollix here – and I know him longer than any of you fuckers – is a genius. Right? Right? This man had the Lord Mayor of Dublin on his fucking knees offering him free houses, when was it? Anyway, some of you were only in short pants. Yes! It's thanks to him, it's because of him that me and youse are, are . . . whatever we are – I'm telling you. Put it all down to him. The laughs, the scams—

STEVIE

The money.

Cheers.]

TONY

Exactly – Michael – Bossman – your Eminence. Any idea how much money we'll get for this holy picture here?

STEVIE

Yeah, like just because it's valued at £30 million—

* Cut from completed film.

URY
MAS
ROBB
Garda

MICHAEL

We'll get enough to be rich, don't worry. And we've won, that's the point. See this . . .

Points to the headlines and the TV. A fancy animation shows graphs of robberies committed (including O'Donnell's) and amount of money stolen.

. . . see all of this? Think about what it means. We're No. 1, not the Gardai, not the IRA, not anyone else – the whole country is in awe of us. We're bigger than Riverdance. We're fuckin' superstars. Thanks to himself there.

They all look at The Taking of Christ, as Michael starts to sing.

One day at a time, Sweet Jesus, that's all I'm asking of you.
Just give me the strength to do all the things that I have to do.

The gang raucously join in the chorus of 'One Day at a Time'.

INT. GARDA HEADQUARTERS – DAY

CU – Michael and Tony on video. Noel is showing Daly and some other officers the security video from the National Gallery. We see the lead up to the actual robbery.

NOEL

Look at these two here.

He points at Michael and Tony.

Watch. I think this is the signal.

On video Michael takes Tony's face in his hands. Immediately the other gang members move to take paintings.

You see, when he does that, everybody moves. The timing is spot on. But it's the signal itself that got me. You see what he's doing, sir?

They watch the moment again. Noel freezes it. Daly and Doyle look at each other, bemused.

DALY

You're right. He's giving a signal, but, ah . . .

NOEL

He's imitating the painting, sir. Look – same as Judas.

Noel indicates Judas and Jesus in the painting, then points to Tony and Michael. Despite themselves the officers nod admiringly.

DALY

Oh right, very clever—

(catches himself)

Well . . . I mean . . .

NOEL

Yeah, it's smart. Obviously someone who likes a gag. That's what made me realise. It's Michael Lynch.

DALY

What? Ah, Noel.

NOEL

We can't make a positive ID from this picture. But look—

On screen is a series of computer-enhanced images comparing the figures of Michael and Tony from the art gallery with real photos of them.

I had body size and shape comparisons done with photos of Lynch and Brady. Heads, height, everything. They match.

DALY

Yes, very interesting Noel, and well done. Good to see the gizmos being put to use and so on. But it's . . . it's coincidence. I mean, your nose alone should tell you Lynch isn't capable of this kind of thing.

NOEL

I went back over the security tapes since the Caravaggio exhibition opened . . . I found this.

Noel plays the tape. It is the Caravaggio room on an ordinary day. He freezes the tape and points at two figures. He zooms in on them.

Lynch and his wife Christine on a day out. I know – I know, it's not evidence of anything – but what's he doing there?

They all watch as Michael is seen to survey the room. Daly is shaken but not stirred.

DALY

No. I'm sorry. We'd look like fools if we presented this idea to the top lads from Interpol. These robberies are the preserve of a few international gangs. Germans, Dutch . . . art thieves who really know their business. Come on Noel, admit it. Lynch is just not in that league.

Noel is frustrated, silent.

INT. OPERATIONS ROOM, GARDA HQ – DAY

Daly and Noel listen to the man from Interpol: Mr De Heer.

DE HEER

It's certainly not the MO of any gang that we know. Which suggests very strongly that it's a very clever local Irish operation and that the painting is still somewhere in your country. You've probably come to that conclusion yourselves already.

Noel remains impassive. Daly improvises.

DALY

Ah yes – oh, indeed. Ah . . .

(not looking at Noel)

Yes, well of course. We are pretty confident at this stage that it's the work of a gang led by Michael Lynch. I'm personally familiar with Lynch's MO, and though *normally*, art theft isn't his thing, this particular robbery seems to have his mark on it all right.

Noel finds Daly's audacity breathtaking.

DE HEER

Good. If you know who you're dealing with it will make a recovery operation much easier. May I offer some further information and perhaps some suggestions?

DALY

(on a roll now)

Absolutely – feel free.

DE HEER

We know that someone here in Dublin has made contact with a fence in Amsterdam. Let us call him Peter. Peter had made contact with us to offer his co-operation . . .

INT. HOTEL NIGHTCLUB – NIGHT

It is noisy and crowded. Michael and Alec drink with Peter. Michael is behaving as drunk as the other two are. A waiter brings another round.

MICHAEL

No, no, Peter, in fairness you've travelled a long way to meet us. You have to let me pay this time.

PETER

Hey, you know it's no problem – you'll be paying the hotel bill anyway.

MICHAEL

(big joke)

Hey, hey, Alec – he's right – so we fucking will. You're a smart fellah, Peter. I like it – I like it.

Peter indicates his room card and signs for the drinks. They toast. Michael slips the room card into his pocket.

MICHAEL

Phone call. Won't be long, I think that slapper over there has her eye on you, Peter.

He nods towards two young ones at the bar and leaves.

INT. HOTEL CORRIDOR – NIGHT

Totally sober now, Michael steps out of the lift and goes to Peter's room. He takes out the room card and opens the door.

INT. PETER'S ROOM – NIGHT

Michael turns on the lights and looks around. He takes some chocolate from the mini-bar and eats as he rummages carefully. In a briefcase he finds what he is looking for: a list of contact numbers, including Commissioner Daly and Dutch Police personnel.

Michael searches further. His attention is caught by a small flashlight. He turns it on and off. He opens it up and finds a small transmitter and microphone inside. He considers what to do. Then grins and replaces it carefully. He leaves the room.

INT. OPS ROOM, GARDA HQ – DAY

Daly steps out of his office and surveys the start of his operation with great satisfaction. Noel sits at his desk unconvinced. Maps

on the wall. Gardai marking where their cars stand ready. Hum of electronic efficiency. New computers, impressive lights etc., all a little scary to Daly.

EXT. PIGEON HOUSE – DAY

Michael, Tony and Stevie are getting into a Hiace van. Alec is going to his car. Michael takes him aside.

MICHAEL

Whatever you do, don't say anything to him about where you're taking him or mention the painting – nothing, OK?

ALEC

(puzzled)

Sure, yeah.

MICHAEL

Not a word, now. Good luck.

EXT./INT. ROAD/CAR – DAY

Alec is driving Peter to the rendezvous. Peter is talking more loudly than he needs to. The torch is sticking up out of his breast pocket. Alec is casually chewing gum and not answering.

PETER

Do you like art generally? What did you think of the painting? It is a beautiful Caravaggio, is it not?

No sign of a reply from Alec. Peter shouts again.

Of course I realise, I suppose, that the money is your main interest. I can tell that you don't like to talk, you have no interest in conversation.

ALEC

No, I love a good chat.

PETER

(pointing)

So this must be the Dublin Mountains, yah?

Alec turns to answer, but instead just nods.

It is – good, good . . . very beautiful. Let's hope the weather remains fine. Especially if we have to view outdoors.

Alec remains coolly silent.

EXT. WOODED AREA, DUBLIN MOUNTAINS – DAY

The van is parked in a small clearing in the woods. Michael opens the back door. Stevie and Tony take out the painting. Michael looks to Peter.

MICHAEL

Where do you want it?

PETER

The Caravaggio?

Michael looks at him but doesn't answer.

Oh, upright somewhere.

MICHAEL

(to Stevie and Tony)

Lean it against the van.

The Taking of Christ is stood upright against the Hiace. Peter takes out his torch and walks towards the painting.

PETER

(loudly)

It's so strange, yes, to be standing here on a wooded mountain top looking at one of the great marvels of Renaissance art. Caravaggio's The Taking of Christ.

As he kneels to look at the painting there is suddenly a gun at his head, held by Michael.

MICHAEL

(icy quiet)

What are you shouting for?

PETER

Oh, I'm sorry, was I? A little excited perhaps. This is a very—

Michael puts his finger to his lips and Peter shuts up. Michael takes the torch from him and makes a show of examining it. He finds the tiny microphone. He shows it to the others.

MICHAEL

(loudly)

Right, Peter, are you happy with your examination?

Nods to him to answer.

PETER

Yes, very happy.

Still holding the gun on him, Michael moves him to Alec's car. Nods to Tony and Stevie to pack up the painting. They move quickly.

MICHAEL

(loudly)

Right, follow me lads – back through Roundwood, OK?

INT. OPS ROOM, GARDA HQ – DAY

Daly is delighted. He checks the map. Noel is beside him with headphones.

DALY

Roundwood . . . got him. OK, Units 2, 3 and 6, Roundwood. If you get there before him I want a complete roadblock.

EXT. SUBURBAN STREET – DAY

A parked Garda car takes off at great speed.

EXT. COUNTRY ROAD – DAY

Detectives hanging around two Garda cars suddenly leap into action, dive for their cars and take off at great speed.

EXT. LAY-BY – DAY

A Garda car screeches on to the road and away.

EXT. ROAD, DUBLIN MOUNTAINS – DAY

Alec's car is followed by the van down the mountain road. Michael sits with his gun trained on the terrified Peter.

MICHAEL

Isn't the scenery around here only fantastic, Peter. Course you've no mountains in Holland, sure you haven't?

He nods to Peter to reply.

PETER

No, very flat, Holland.

Michael nods for more. Peter racks his brain.

I love your country very much.

MICHAEL

Same here, Peter. Ireland is a great place to live, do you know that. Are we near Roundwood yet?

ALEC

(playing along)

Ah, about half a mile; once we get off this road we're as good as there.

MICHAEL

Fantastic. We might stop for a pint, will we?

EXT. WICKLOW MOUNTAIN ROAD – DAY

Unmarked cars hurtle towards Roundwood. They whiz past a tiny mountain road. Once they are out of sight, Alec's car and the van appear and turn in the opposite direction towards Dublin.

INT. OPS ROOM GARDA HQ – DAY

Great excitement as Daly talks to his units.

DALY

Are you in position? I want that roadblock rock solid, do you hear me? Nothing, repeat nothing, is to get through.

Noel turns to Daly.

NOEL

Sir, the surveillance plane can't spot the subject anywhere near Roundwood.

DALY

What? What's he talking about?

NOEL

He says they're not in the area.

DALY

Well they have to be. Maybe they haven't come out of the woods yet.

INT. ALEC'S CAR – DAY

They are driving through dense Dublin working-class suburbs.

MICHAEL

Here we go. There's Roundwood up ahead Peter, supposed to be the highest village in Ireland. Wouldn't mind living around here I can tell you – a lovely quiet spot.

Nods to Peter who looks at the teeming life on the streets.

PETER

Yes, very tranquil.

INT. OPS ROOM, GARDA HQ – DAY

Daly is mystified.

DALY

They're just coming into Roundwood now.

NOEL

(deadpan)

Well, the surveillance plane still can't see them.

DALY

What's going on – fuck – fuck – oh God forgive me.

EXT. GARDA HQ – DAY

Alec stops the car outside the Garda station.

MICHAEL

What an awful waste of taxpayers' money.

They dump Peter out on the road. He is gagged with the microphone still in his shirt pocket. The gang drive off.

INT. OPS ROOM, GARDA HQ – DAY

Daly is surprised at what he has just heard.

DALY

What's he talking about?

Then they hear.

PETER

(off)

N-n-n-n-n-ahhhh . . .

Noel knows he will be empowered by Daly's cock-up.

EXT. GARDA HQ – DAY

Peter is picking himself up and trying to talk into the microphone with a gag on.

PETER

(muffled)

They're right here outside the station. Hurry, for Christ's sake!

EXT. PIGEON HOUSE – DAY

Alec's car followed by the van pulls into the warehouse at speed. Alec lets out a yell as he looks in awe at Michael.

ALEC

Yow! That was just fucking amazing – what a buzz.

Tony and Stevie pass by with the Caravaggio. Stevie just looks grim and says nothing. Tony bangs on the window.

TONY

Come on – let's move.

Alec jumps out to help. They disappear up the steps to the office. Michael sits back and smirks to himself. He is very buzzed by his latest gag. Tony returns. He opens the car door. Angry.

You knew all along, didn't you?

MICHAEL

How do you mean?

TONY

Like . . . explain it to me. What did we go through all that for if you knew Peter was a fake?

Michael grins as if he might not know himself.

MICHAEL

They're going to feel so stupid. The Gardai are going to think now there's no way they can ever get the better of us.

TONY

(dubious)

Yeah, maybe . . . I wouldn't try that one with Stevie right now.

MICHAEL

Stevie? Fuck him if he has no sense of humour.

*[INT. LISA'S BEDROOM – DAY

A baby is plucked out of a cot.

Michael picks up his latest son. Lisa is in bed. Christine is sitting on the bed with her. They cheer as Michael holds the baby high.

MICHAEL

How're ya doing, kid. Show me you – who do you look like?

LISA

Us, he's a Shanahan.

CHRISTINE

He is, Michael.

Michael kisses his cheek. He looks at Christine and Lisa smiling. Something occurs to him.

MICHAEL

Do you think I should call it a day, girls?

LISA

You can say that again. I'm having no more, anyway.

MICHAEL

No, no . . . I mean work.

* Cut from completed film.

LISA

What?

CHRISTINE

You . . . retire like? Yeah, sure.

LISA

You couldn't stay off the mooch for a week even.

MICHAEL

No, the thing is . . . I can't do anything better than the last job. It would just seem like Mickey Mouse stuff, you know.

CHRISTINE

But you'd drive us mad.

LISA

Hanging around under our feet day and night. No fuckin' way, Michael.

MICHAEL

I wouldn't, I swear. Anyway you can pass me over and back between ye.

CHRISTINE

True. D'you really want to?

Michael looks at the baby.

MICHAEL

Ah yeah. I think so. You know what politicians say when they get fucked out. I want to spend more time with my family.]

FADE TO BLACK

INT. MICHAEL'S BEDROOM – NIGHT

Michael lies in bed next to sleeping Christine. He is looking at the Caravaggio poster on the wall.

CU of the Judas kiss.

Michael smiles.

EXT. JESUIT COMMUNITY HOUSE – DAY

Michael parks. He gets out and unfastens the wooden frame.

INT. JESUIT COMMUNITY HOUSE – DAY

Mass is in progress in the room converted into a little community chapel. About twelve priests are present.

Father Grogan, the celebrant, has his back to the window and all the other priests are kneeling with their heads bowed. So they do not see . . .

FATHER GROGAN

The night before He suffered He took bread and gave thanks and praise. He broke the bread, gave it to His disciples . . .

. . . out the window behind Father Grogan, Michael walking around a corner carrying the wooden frame, approaching the house.

EXT. JESUIT COMMUNITY HOUSE – DAY

Michael arrives at the window directly below where mass is being celebrated. He breaks in easily and quietly.

INT. BASEMENT ROOM, JESUIT COMMUNITY HOUSE – DAY

The sounds of mass can be heard faintly. Michael takes down the replica and replaces it with the original Caravaggio. As he does so, the sound of the priest saying mass can be heard. Michael stands back to look at his work in satisfaction.

He puts the replica into the frame. Checks that everything is as it should be. He leaves by the back door.

EXT./INT. JESUIT COMMUNITY HOUSE – DAY

As Michael walks away carrying the wooden frame, the camera cranes up and tracks back into the room where mass is being celebrated to find the priests all standing holding hands and praying in unison.

PRIEST

Thank you Lord for the gifts which you have bestowed on us your unworthy servants . . .

EXT. MICHAEL'S HOUSE – EARLY MORNING

Two unmarked cars drive up and park outside Michael's house. Noel, Ger, Liam and Luke step out. They don't speak. They look relaxed. Noel in particular looks pleased. They lounge against their cars and light up.

From now on the Gardai are seen at very close quarters. They seem different; younger, tougher, sharper. Most of them we have never seen before. Noel's men.

INT. MICHAEL'S BEDROOM – MORNING

Michael is asleep. Christine in her dressing-gown comes in looking worried. She wakes him.

CHRISTINE

Michael . . . Micha-e-l. Take a look at what's happening outside.

MICHAEL

What?

CHRISTINE

Just look. Front and back.

Michael gets out of bed and goes to the window that looks down on his back garden. Peeks out.

Three detectives are perched on the wall at the end of the garden drinking tea.

Michael looks at Christine who shrugs.

MICHAEL

How did they get there?

He goes to the front of the house.

INT. KIDS' BEDROOM – MORNING

The children are still asleep as Michael comes through their room. Looks out the window on to the road outside.

Noel, Ger, Liam and Luke are still lounging at their cars. Noel spots Michael. He waves up to him.

MICHAEL

What's going on?

Now Tony, Alec and Stevie all arrive, each with two unmarked cars following. Michael and Christine stare in shock as ten cars crowd for space outside his front garden. Another gang of detectives casually step out of their cars and just hang around outside the house.

INT. BEDROOM, MICHAEL'S HOUSE – DAY

Michael finishes applying black boot polish to his face. He looks a bit like Al Jolson. Stevie, Alec and Tony stand around, variously hooded and masked.

MICHAEL

They're still there? Out in the open?

EXT. MICHAEL'S HOUSE – DAY

Christine peeps out the window. The detectives giver her a little wave.

INT. BEDROOM, MICHAEL'S HOUSE – DAY

CHRISTINE

Yeah.

Michael pulls up his hood. Looks at the others.

MICHAEL

Come on, so. We see what they're up to. This is some new thing, but remember, whatever they do – ignore them. They don't exist.

Christine opens the front door. The gang go out to the gridlock.

EXT. MICHAEL'S HOUSE – DAY

Michael and the others walk to their cars. They do not acknowledge the presence of all these detectives who talk loudly.

LUKE

That him, yeah?

GER

Yeah. Look at the state of him and his pals.

LUKE

That baldy fuck is supposed to be a criminal mastermind? You must be joking. He's just a thick gobshite who got lucky, I'd say.

GER

Well, he's fucked now. They're all fucked.

The gang manage to keep their cool. The detectives follow.

EXT. MICHAEL'S HOUSE – DAY

One of the unmarked cars pulls alongside Michael's car, blocking his departure.

GER

You can feel it, can't you? Hey Lynch, are you listening? You might as well give up now, because we're going to be glued to your arse from now on.

Michael ignores them. But he is worried, trying to figure out what's going on. Ger and Noel wave to him and pull in front of him.

EXT. MOUNTAINSIDE – EVENING

We are back up the mountains, only this time the detectives' car is right on top of Michael's. Michael stops and gets out. Noel and Ger step out also, watching. Michael, smiling slightly, goes to the boot and opens it. He takes out the five gallon drum as before, and turns to Noel with a smirk.

Noel is standing there also holding up a five gallon drum. Ger, grinning 'fuck you', is beside him.

Reaction from Michael. Things are not going to be so easy any more.

INT. MICHAEL'S HOUSE – DAY

Lisa, baby in arms, and Christine are having a natter. Michael bursts in, in a vile temper.

MICHAEL

Girls, have ye a minute.

LISA

What's up with you?

MICHAEL

Nothing, it's just these fucking Gardai. Getting on my nerves. I want you to drive me later.

LISA

And where are the guards going to be?

MICHAEL

Are you going to fucking help me or not?

LISA

Yeah – sure, keep your hair on.

Michael tries to control himself.

EXT. WINETAVERN STREET – DAY

In the heart of Dublin, Michael's car, Alec's car, Stevie's car and Tony's car all block the street. Lisa and other wives/girlfriends are passengers. Each car is pursued by two detective cars.

The four boys Michael, Alec, Stevie and Tony hop out casually and dart into an alleyway. Clearly a prearranged scam. They run off together talking, leaving chaos behind as detectives leap out of their cars to run after the gang. Lisa steps out and talks to no one in particular as Noel tries to clamber over her car and get past her. Cars build up behind the Gardai cars, honking horns.

LISA

Could somebody call the Guards? Sort out this mess. They're never around when you need them.

Noel pushes past.

NOEL

His time is up, Lisa. It's way past a joke, and I think you know it.

Maybe she does.

EXT. QUAY AT WINETAVERN STREET BRIDGE – DAY

Michael, Stevie, Alec and Tony walk fast along the bridge and on to the quay. The detectives are still running to catch up. Michael winks at passers-by enjoying the recognition. The gang seem less happy at all this.

TONY

How can they keep this up? How many have they doing this?

STEVIE

There must be a hundred. And I don't know any of them.

MICHAEL

Don't worry, once we figure out what their game is we can deal with it.

EXT. HA'PENNY BRIDGE – DAY

The gang turn off the quay and on to the bridge. They walk fast, talk fast.

STEVIE

Have you been able to shake them off?

Michael and Tony shake their heads.

TONY

It's doing my head in.

MICHAEL

Don't let it. Keep smiling at them.

STEVIE

I've had a contact about the painting, Michael.

MICHAEL

Yeah?

STEVIE

An offer. From the IRA.

Michael keeps walking. No visible reaction. Detectives appear in the distance. The gang move even faster.

A straightforward, no bullshit offer. £100,000. Not great, I know, but better than having the thing just rot away. And – ah – your man Higgins said if you did the deal it would be all right about Billy.

MICHAEL

Sorry?

STEVIE

Like you could let him come back to Dublin. There'd be no hassle.

MICHAEL

You talked to Higgins about Billy?

STEVIE

Look if we do this, those fuckers will go after the IRA and let us alone.

Alec finds the courage to speak up.

ALEC

Anyway, it's not our thing. You know – art stuff. We're not in that league.

The wrong thing to say. Stevie and Alec have blown it.

MICHAEL

See all these Gardai. Look what we've done to them. We've *dragged* them down to our level. They're acting like criminals now. I'm their worst fucking nightmare. And you're telling me we should give up this painting, the thing we'll be remembered for, and hand it over to Higgins of all people? You think he'll give you a hundred grand?

STEVIE

Yes.

MICHAEL

Like fuck – can't you see what he's at? It's not about the painting, it's about splitting us.

STEVIE

All I know is we're robbers, Michael. We rob for a living. I'm not making a living any more.

MICHAEL

I know that.

A moment. Stevie and Michael understand each other.

There's stuff you want. You need money, I know.

TONY

Well look, Michael – will you think about it – what we've been saying? Michael?

MICHAEL

Yeah. Tell Higgins I'll let him know.

STEVIE

I'll be letting him know, too. Hope we're telling him the same thing.

The gang walks off as several detectives, including Noel, catch up with Michael. Michael ignores them but suddenly looks at his watch.

MICHAEL

My God, is that the time. I'll be late picking up the kids.

He walks off smartly, Noel following at his shoulder.

INT. DOLE OFFICE – DAY

Michael, Alec and Tony, enter the Dole Office still pursued by Noel and the other detectives.

Michael arrives at the counter. He leans forward as he always does to the nervous Clerk.

MICHAEL

Michael Lynch. How are you today?

The Clerk hands him a slip of paper. Michael looks at it.

What's this?

CLERK

Ah – your benefits have been – ah – rescinded.

MICHAEL

Try that one again.

CLERK

It's the government. I just got the order. You see . . . they've cut off your dole.

Michael stares at him. The silence around the Dole Office is awesome. Every person feels the chill and waits, tense and alert. Ger, Larry, Luke and Noel are ready to move in if there's serious trouble.

I'm just . . . I got the order. So I have to – I can't . . .

This is the last straw for Michael. He turns and eyeballs Noel. For the first time it looks like he might break. Noel certainly hopes so. But instead he turns back to the Clerk and hisses at him.

MICHAEL

You think you can break me like this? You're off your fucking head. *(shouts)* You're off your fucking head.

INT. MICHAEL'S HOUSE

We hear Noel's voice outside shouting in.

NOEL

(off)

Hey, Lynch. This is Noel Quigley. Big mistake last night, or do you even know that. What was that supposed to be? Funny? Was that your idea of a joke, you ugly bag of shit. You're losing it Lynch, so fast.

CHRISTINE

Can't you see where it's all heading, Michael?

MICHAEL

I see now what they're trying to do—

CHRISTINE

Only the one way. You in prison and it'll be twenty years. More maybe. And me and Lisa and the kids will be left—

MICHAEL

No – that's not gonna happen.

NOEL

(off)

As long as you live, we'll be here watching you, do you get it? No escape.

EXT. MICHAEL'S HOUSE – DAY

Christine opens the door and shouts at Noel and the others.

CHRISTINE

Stop it! Stop it! Will you stop it! Leave us alone!

Christine slams the door.

INT. MICHAEL'S HOUSE – DAY

MICHAEL

Don't let them see that we're—

CHRISTINE

Fuck off, Michael.

INT. STAIRS/BEDROOM, MICHAEL'S HOUSE – DAY

Christine walks upstairs. Michael follows.

MICHAEL

I promise you, Christine – no matter what – they'll never put me away.

CHRISTINE

They're out to get you – what can you do about it?

MICHAEL

What can I . . .? I'll tell you, I . . . I don't know.

Christine stops and turns. Michael looks clearly at her.

I'm afraid, OK . . . I'm afraid you might be right. It's never happened to me before but I'm not sure now – I don't know what it is? Will they wear me down bit by bit until – 'cause, 'cause they can't get the better of me any other way – I won't let them. Never. I mean if that happens, then . . . then it was all worth nothing.

CHRISTINE

Well what are we going to do, so?

MICHAEL

I don't know.

Michael's whole body is tight with tension.

CHRISTINE

What about the painting? If you got some money—

MICHAEL

Sure that was never about the money. To be honest, I haven't a clue how to unload it. Got a few great laughs out of it though.

Christine holds him. Kisses him.

CHRISTINE

Do you know what you are . . . you're irrepressible, you're inimitable.

MICHAEL

That good, yeah?

CHRISTINE

Well – it wouldn't be every one's cup of tea. But it suits me.

She smiles and they kiss again. Fuller, longer this time. Michael begins to pull at her clothes. They fall on the floor, Christine laughing loudly.

EXT. MICHAEL'S HOUSE – DAY

The detectives hanging around outside can hear the laughter. They recognise the sounds of spirited lovemaking. Noel looks at the others in disbelief.

EXT. FUNERAL PARLOUR – DAY

Classic Mafia movie shot. The entrance to the funeral parlour. Noel and other detectives stand outside, in that formal way they do. Tony's car pulls up followed by his detective team. They get out and stand outside. The shot now has a posed look to it. Tony goes to the entrance, looks around before going in. Shakes his head.

TONY

Fuck's sake.

INT. FUNERAL PARLOUR – DAY

Michael is inside examining coffins.

MICHAEL

I've been fucking you around, haven't I?

TONY

You have, Michael. That's what you've been doing all right.

MICHAEL

I was out of order – I'm sorry.

TONY

It's all right – what do you expect with all this . . .

They look out at Noel and co.

MICHAEL

But whatever Stevie's up to will only make things worse. You know that, don't you?

TONY

No I don't. He's only trying to sort things out. Get us back to where we were.

MICHAEL

And that's what Higgins wants? Do you really believe that?

TONY

What choice have we? You're not helping.

They stand near the window. Noel and Ger are looking directly in at them.

MICHAEL

Would you say any of those fellahs can lip-read? You'd be amazed the skills Gardai have these days.

(pronounces very deliberately)

Ye're fantastic lads, do you know that?

TONY

Michael—

MICHAEL

OK, OK. Do one thing for me. Tell me what's next. He's going to try and get the painting to Higgins, right? With or without me. Come on, we all know that. Tony. How does he think ye'll get away from the Gardai?

Tony hesitates.

TONY

It's a good plan. I think it'll work.

MICHAEL

Fair enough. Go on, what is it? Trust me, will you?

TONY

You know Copeland Grove?

EXT. SUMMERHILL STREET – DAY

We see Summerhill, a quiet residential street. It is a cul-de-sac with steps leading out of it.

MICHAEL

(off)

Yeah?

TONY

(off)

It's a cul-de-sac, right. With steps at the end.

MICHAEL

(off)

Leading on to Summerhill. You're going to drive up there . . .

Three cars driven by Stevie, Alec and Tony turn into the street followed by the usual squad of detectives.

How though? All together? One car's no good.

TONY

(off)

No.

MICHAEL

(off)

A car each, enough to block the road . . . yeah . . . not bad if you can work it right . . .

As the three gang cars near the top of the street, they go into a spin, turning swiftly so that between them they block the road and pathway.

TONY

(off)

I don't see why we can't. Give us enough time to get up the lane to Summerhill.

Stevie, Tony and Alec all jump out of their cars at the same moment and run to the steps. All the detectives skid to a halt and try to get out of their cars fast enough, clambering over the gang's cars.

MICHAEL

(off)

You'll have a car waiting—?

TONY

(off)

A van.

MICHAEL

(off)

Of course, yeah – for the painting. That'll work all right. Alec will move it out lively enough.

EXT. SUMMERHILL – DAY

Stevie, Tony and Alec come running down steps and on to the street, where a green Hiace is parked. They jump in.

TONY

(off)

Yeah. Once we get away from the Gardai all we have to do is—

MICHAEL

(off)

Hold on a minute.

INT. FUNERAL PARLOUR – DAY

MICHAEL

That's where it'll happen.

TONY

What?

MICHAEL

You'll get away from the Gardai. I bet you will – easily. 'Cause I think they'll be tipped off. Look! Which is better for Higgins – he buys a painting he can't get rid of, or he has all of Michael Lynch's gang arrested in one go. Leaving just me to come after in his own good time.

Tony looks uncertain.

Believe me; don't believe me. All I'm saying is watch very carefully . . .

INT./EXT. HIACE VAN/ROAD – DAY

Stevie and Tony sit in the back of the van as Alec drives. Stevie talking animatedly.

MICHAEL

(off)

. . . when you get in that van, make sure you can see everything that's going on around you. Think about it – Higgins or Stevie – who would the smart money be on?

Tony watches very carefully.

As soon as you take off, a car will appear from somewhere – nice and casual. Then you'll know, Tony. It's all I'm asking. Look out for it.

STEVIE

The way me and Higgins see it, if we are reasonable we can divide up the work. Co-operate. Let each other know what we're doing, that kind of thing, so we don't get in each other's way. In fact, the opposite.

TONY

What exactly are you after getting us into?

STEVIE

This is the kind of thing Higgins says we'll be able to get in on. We're finally getting rid of these paintings, right? £100 grand, right? Now while we have the filth running around like bluearse flies wondering where we're gone, Higgins has some of his crowd robbing the bank on Dame Street.

TONY

I can't believe what I'm hearing.

STEVIE

And – wait – and he's promised me a cut of that on top of the £100 grand. That's just for us – none for Michael. Two scams happening at the same time – the filth don't know where to look. They can't handle it. It works better for us all.

Tony sees from the back window a car appear, it seems, out of nowhere and follow them up the road. Can he see Noel in it?

TONY

(off)

And if you're right?

MICHAEL

(off)

What do you think? Get the fuck out of that van as fast as you can.

Tony is trying to make up his mind what to do. He looks at Stevie jabbering away, madly excited. He looks back at the pursuing car. Surely it is Noel.

And as soon as you get away, phone me, or don't if you like. Your choice. But I promise – I'll be waiting.

CU – Tony in the van. What to do?

INT. FUNERAL PARLOUR – DAY

Michael is examining coffins with the Undertaker.

MICHAEL

This is nice, isn't it.

TONY

Yeah, lovely.

MICHAEL

(to Undertaker)

Put that one away for me, will you. I'll need it in a few days.

UNDERTAKER

Yes, sir.

As the Undertaker goes off, Michael and Tony make to leave.

MICHAEL

What do you think? Did I make the right choice? It's a bit dear, but what the hell. You only die once.

TONY

Give us a break, will you.

INT. MICHAEL'S HOUSE – DAY

CU – phone in hallway. It is ringing really loudly.

Michael picks up the phone. Throughout this conversation the focus is on Michael looking at Lisa and Christine as they go about their morning oblivious to what's happening.

TONY

(off)

Michael – it's Tony. You were right. It's a fuck-up.

MICHAEL

OK. OK. Are you free? There's no one on to you?

TONY

(off)

Yeah, I'm in Dorset Street—

MICHAEL

(delighted)

Jesus, yes! So did you find out anything? Where's Higgins supposed to pick up the paintings?

TONY

(off)

It's better than that. Higgins is going to pull a bank job at the same time as the paintings are collected. With half the Gardai in Dublin chasing Stevie and Alec up the mountains.

MICHAEL

Where – do you know?

TONY

(off)

Yeah, Dame Street, Stevie said.

MICHAEL

OK, listen. Go there now. Fast. Check it out. But make sure you're not being followed. Ring me from there in fifteen minutes. What are you wearing, by the way?

TONY

(off)

What?

MICHAEL

What are you wearing?

TONY

(off)

Blue jeans, red shirt, jumper – you know the one – wax jacket.

MICHAEL

Good – talk to you.

He puts down the phone, still looking at Christine and Lisa through the gap in the kitchen door. He is entirely alert and animated now.

INT. MICHAEL'S BEDROOM – DAY

Michael is dressing himself. As he does so we can see a plan forming in his head. He puts a spare balaclava and coat into a little bag. He picks up a gun. The phone rings again.

INT. MICHAEL'S HOUSE – DAY

Michael on the phone to Tony.

TONY

(off)

Everything normal in the bank so far. Maybe Stevie was bullshitting.

MICHAEL

I don't think so. I think we're in business. OK, Tony, are you listening?

TONY

(off)

Yeah.

MICHAEL

Here's what's going to happen. You hang around inside the bank. I'll wait outside . . .

INT. MICHAEL'S HOUSE – DAY

Michael is still on the phone.

MICHAEL

And you come here to my place, with the cash.

TONY

(off)

What about you, Michael?

MICHAEL

How do you mean?

TONY

(off)

So I get away. What happens to you?

MICHAEL

Ah, Tony – you don't expect me to have all the answers, do you?

TONY

Michael—

MICHAEL

See you in the bank, Tony – soon.

He puts the phone down. Looks again at Christine and Lisa sitting inside drinking tea.

CHRISTINE

Well?

MICHAEL

What?

CHRISTINE

Have you two kissed and made up.

MICHAEL

Me and Tony? Yeah, of course—

CHRISTINE

Good. You can't be falling out with friends like him.

MICHAEL

Listen, ah . . . girls.

The women look at him expectantly.

I think I'll be able to – you know, fix things. You know, so you're not left walking the streets begging.

LISA

'Course you will.

CHRISTINE

We're not worried. Are we?

MICHAEL

Sure, yeah sure – I just wanted you to know, you know – it's on my mind, right. Like . . . I'm lookin' after things.

LISA

What? Are we supposed to be crying we're so grateful, like?

CHRISTINE

Ah, let him alone, he's only – you know. Don't worry. It's grand, Michael.

MICHAEL

Yeah right, yeah—

CHRISTINE

Go on so – get out from under our feet.

EXT. DAME STREET BANK – DAY

Michael comes to a halt across the road from the bank entrance. He sits back and waits. He looks in complete control.

Liam and Larry tuck in behind him and wait. They look at each other, a little puzzled.

EXT. DAME STREET BANK – DAY

Michael tenses as he sees a car pull up outside the bank. Two IRA Men step out and walk quickly towards the bank. One man remains in the driver's seat. It is Shay.

MICHAEL

As soon as the IRA lads arrive, we're off and running.

Michael smiles to himself and steps off his bike. He follows the two IRA Men quickly, although as he does he passes their car and taps Shay's window.

Liam and Larry have sat up as soon as Michael left his bike. They notice the tap and see Shay. He, unaware of their presence, jumps out of the car to go after Michael who disappears into the bank.

INT. BANK – DAY

Michael enters the bank and catches Tony's eye. He nods towards the IRA Men. Tony understands and waits as the two IRA Men meet up with another man whose face is hidden from view.

EXT. DAME STREET BANK – DAY

Shay hesitates outside the entrance, clearly not sure what he should do. As he turns to go back to the car he comes face to face with the approaching detectives. He realises who they are and pulls his gun. They're close enough to jump on him and smother him as he falls back on the ground.

INT. BANK – DAY

The three IRA Men pull guns. There is the usual screaming and panic. Michael drops face down like the ordinary customers and Tony follows suit. They wait patiently as the robbery begins.

EXT. DAME STREET BANK – DAY

The detectives drag a struggling Shay to their car. They handcuff him and push him into the car.

LIAM

Better ask for assistance.

He goes for his radio.

LIAM

Foxtrot One calling. Request urgent assistance. We have a situation here.

CONTROL

(off)

Are you off your head? Urgent assistance with six armed units chasing after that fucking painting?

INT. OFFICE, PIGEON HOUSE – DAY

Stevie and Alec lift The Taking of Christ off the wall. They start downstairs with it.

INT. PIGEON HOUSE – DAY

Alec and Stevie are hidden by the painting as they carry it along the upper level from Michael's office. Below, in the shadows by the door, the detectives wait: Noel and Ger with an armed response unit.

NOEL

Stop where you are. You have no chance of escape.

The painting hesitates, moves this way then that; unsure for a moment, behind the painting Alec looks round the frame at the Garda presence below.

ALEC

Fuck. Michael wouldn't have got us into this mess.

STEVIE

What the fuck'll we do?

ALEC

Here goes.

INT. BANK – DAY

The three IRA Men are now backing away towards the door with the loot, guns in hand, still unaware that anything is amiss. Michael and Tony watch each other across the floor of the bank. Michael winks and goes for his gun. So does Tony. They shoot one IRA Man who falls. The second IRA Man goes for the door, shooting wildly. The third drops his gun as Michael stands aiming directly at him. He pulls off the IRA Man's balaclava. It is Higgins.

MICHAEL

Ah, good – Jerome.

EXT. DAME STREET BANK – DAY

The IRA Man runs out still firing and turns towards the getaway car to see Liam and Larry armed and waiting behind the car. Panicked, he aims to fire but he is shot first. He falls wounded.

INT. PIGEON HOUSE – DAY

Noel looks at the painting rushing up the steps back towards Michael's office, Alec and Stevie well hidden behind it. The other detectives look to him for instructions.

NOEL

Fuck art.

He fires with his automatic rifle. The painting falters, bullet-ridden, and falls. Alec and Stevie lie dead beneath the Caravaggio.

INT. BANK – DAY

Tony is now wearing the spare anorak and stuffing himself with money: it goes inside his jacket, down his trousers. Higgins is now disarmed and lying down, with the customers. Michael guards them.

EXT. DAME STREET BANK – DAY

Larry is dragging the wounded IRA Man to the car as a very agitated Liam talks urgently on the radio. A crowd has, of course, begun to gather.

LIAM

There is an armed robbery in progress. Must have urgent assistance. Lynch is involved. This is a highly dangerous situation.

CONTROL

(off)

Doing our best – I have some unarmed units on their way.

LIAM

For fuck's sake – we need armed assistance urgently – there's only two of us. There's three men armed and dangerous in there. One of them is Michael Lynch, do you understand?

INT. PIGEON HOUSE – DAY

Ger holds up the destroyed painting. Grins at Noel.

GER

I hope they don't take it out of your wages.

LENNIE

Sorry Noel, getting urgent calls – an armed robbery in progress at a bank on Dame Street. They're still inside. One of them is Lynch.

NOEL

Fuck – oh, fuck – how did he . . .? Let's move now.

He runs to the door.

Keep him there – whatever they do, tell them, keep him there.

(very melodramatic)

Lynch is mine.

*[INT. BANK – DAY

Michael is buttoning up a fatter-looking Tony. He pulls the hood well over his face. Once again he looks just like Michael. He gives him the bike keys.

MICHAEL

(off)

Now we have to make them think I'm surrendering. This is your big moment, Tony 'cause they won't know about you at all. No one has seen you. Take a look at where my bike is out there.

Tony does so.

You go out. They'll bring you to their car just behind. Whatever you do, don't let them find out it's not me until then. Remember, they don't know what's happening; they've got two prisoners to watch out there already. They're terrified—

TONY

Sure, Michael, but listen to me—

MICHAEL

I'll be watching. When I see you're at the car I'll start a diversion. That's when you have to go. You have the money, so you'd better get away. Do you hear me, fuckface.

TONY

Yeah? And what'll you do?

* Cut from completed film.

MICHAEL

Don't ask stupid questions. Trust me.

TONY

Yeah, I do – but I don't see how—

MICHAEL

Will you stop arguing. You'll get us both killed.

(shouts)

Hey lads – Michael Lynch talking to you. Can you hear me?

LIAM

(off)

Yes.

TONY

Michael, just tell me—

MICHAEL

(shouting)

I'm coming out. I'm giving myself up, OK.

(quietly to Tony)

Ready?

(shouting)

What do you want me to do?

LIAM

(off)

Hold your hands clearly in the air and come out slowly. Keep walking towards us until we tell you to stop.

MICHAEL

(shouts)

OK, here I come lads – Youse fellahs are going to be heroes, do you know that?

(quietly to Tony)

Relax, OK – eye on the ball.

Michael winks at Tony who looks at him helplessly, then raising his hands in the air, turns and walks out.]

EXT. DAME STREET BANK – DAY

Liam and Larry look at each other in disbelief as the notorious Michael Lynch appears to walk out of the bank with his hands high in the air.

INT. BANK – DAY

Michael watches. Higgins thinks about moving. At the last moment Michael turns on him.

MICHAEL

I thought you IRA fellahs had stopped wanting to be martyrs.

He looks back outside as Tony reaches the detectives.

EXT. DAME STREET BANK – DAY

Liam and Larry grab Tony; they take an arm each and back him towards their car. They are very frightened.

LARRY

OK, what's going on, Lynch? Who's left in there?

LIAM

What are you up to, Lynch?

No answer. They reach the car.

Right, get that thing off your face. It's the last time you'll wear it.

Tony looks at them. Looks at where Michael's bike is.

Fuck you – do what you're told, all right!

INT. BANK – DAY

Michael waits, looking out the gap in the door. The tension from everyone in the bank is incredible. Michael's concentration is absolute.

EXT. DAME STREET BANK – DAY

LIAM

All right. It's coming off whether you like it or not.

Liam reaches forward and pulls the hood back. Tony grins.

TONY

How're you.

They can't believe it.

INT. BANK – DAY

Michael pushes Higgins out of sight of the customers and bank workers.

MICHAEL

Right lads, up ye get, one by one and walk out with your hands held high. Come on, move it. I'm setting you free, folks, don't waste my time.

Somewhat in shock, the plain folk stand up one by one as Michael motions them out. They go like scared rabbits, expecting to be shot at any moment.

INT. BANK – DAY

Michael kicks open the door of the bank and, letting out a terrifying roar, fires at the detectives.

Larry drags Tony down with him but he kicks him, leaps over the bonnet of the car and runs towards Michael's Kawasaki. The IRA Man and Shay try to break free in the car. Pandemonium.

EXT. DAME STREET BANK – DAY

Liam and Larry recover to see the hostages emerge from the bank calling not to be shot. By the time they look around Tony has already started Michael's bike and pulled away. The hostages still pour out. Liam and Larry don't know what to do. We see a quick shot of the Kawasaki disappearing safely.

EXT. DAME STREET BANK – DAY

A scene of turmoil as Noel and other detectives finally arrive. Liam and Larry try to get the hostages out of harm's way. Noel goes to them.

NOEL

What's happening?

LIAM

I haven't a clue, but Lynch is still in there.

NOEL

(pleased, determined)

Good.

*[INT. BANK – DAY

Michael holds a gun to Higgins' head while pulling the balaclava down over Higgins' face.

MICHAEL

Good man. Now take this.

Michael gives him a gun, emptying the magazine.

He pushes the furious Higgins out the door.]

EXT. DAME STREET BANK – DAY

Suddenly Michael Lynch appears to emerge from the bank. A silence falls as he steps forward falteringly. Noel can't believe the moment has come.

* Cut from completed film

NOEL

Keep your hands up, Lynch. Remove the hood. Now. Take it off, Lynch. Come forward slowly.

*[INT. BANK – DAY

Michael watches Higgins progress towards the top of the steps. He prepares to fire.]

EXT. DAME STREET BANK – DAY

Higgins hesitates at the top of the steps. Raises his hands to take the balaclava off. But one of his hands has a gun in it.

*[INT. BANK – DAY

Michael watches this moment and quickly lets off a wild shot.]

EXT. DAME STREET BANK – DAY

Noel reacts to the shot instinctively. He fires. Higgins is almost blown away as other police open fire. Higgins takes many hits to the head.

An eerie silence. Noel watches as the Gardai rush to the body.

Noel turns to a young detective.

* Cut from completed film.

NOEL

(calmly)

Contact Lynch's wife. Tell her she has to come and identify his body.

EXT. BACK OF BANK – DAY

Silhouette of Michael walking along roof ladder to another building and freedom.

SUDDEN CUT TO:

INT. MICHAEL'S HOUSE – DAY

Michael's front door. Someone hammering ferociously on it. Christine opens the door and Tony staggers in. He opens his jacket and money pours out. He looks at Christine; she knows what's happened. She opens her mouth and screams.

CHRISTINE

Michael! No! Michael!

Lisa rushes in and grabs her as she falls down on the money.

The phone rings and rings. Lisa goes and grabs it.

LISA

Yes . . . what? Yes.

She puts down the phone. They want someone to go down and identify Michael's body.

INT. MORTUARY – DAY

Christine and Lisa, both rather distraught, arrive at the mortuary. They are met by Daly and Noel.

DALY

Are you Michael Lynch's wife Christine?

Even now, the women don't talk to Gardai.

And you are his . . . sister-in-law – Lisa?

Still no acknowledgement. Daly sighs.

Right. Will you formally identify this body as that of your husband Michael Lynch. A nod will do.

The girls brush past them and go to where the corpse is laid out. They are in deep distress.

The Attendant uncovers the face. The girls look. The damage caused by the shots means they can't see if it is Michael's face. They ask the Attendant to remove the sheet from the body. He does so.

The women look at the body. It is clearly not Michael. They glance at each other. What's going on?

The women will not look at Noel. He does not look at them.

NOEL

Can you identify your husband?

The women exchange glances again. The truth begins to dawn. The smallest of smiles appear on their faces. They look at the unfortunate corpse again. They suppress the smile. Noel and Daly do not see this. With some effort they intone . . .

CHRISTINE

Yes. This is the body of my husband, Michael Lynch.

LISA

Yes – this is Michael Lynch.

They turn to go. Noel looks after them.

DALY

Right. It's over.

(sincerely to Noel)

Well done.

INT. CHURCH – DAY

Track back from a coffin bedecked with flowers. The same coffin Michael had been looking at in the Funeral Parlour scene. From loudspeakers on either side a song plays 'You Left Me Just When I Needed You Most'.

LOUDSPEAKER

'I woke this morning and I
Stared out the window and I
Tried to think of something to say . . .'

In the congregation we see a very dignified Christine and Lisa with baby in arms. We detect only the hint of a smile from either

of them. The children are all beautifully turned out for the occasion. Billy is back. He is too wired to hide his enjoyment of the situation.

> *'You left without even closing the door*
> *I didn't stand in your way*
> *Now I need you more*
> *Than I did before . . .'*

INT. CHURCH – DAY

Noel and Ger amongst a troop of Gardai and a crowd of gawkers standing around waiting for the service to end. The song continues in the background over this scene.

GER

You did the right thing. We're all better off without him.

Noel doesn't react. He is preoccupied.

GER

Lynch would love this send-off. He's probably up there somewhere having a laugh at the idea of us protecting him.

Noel has been looking at the women and at Billy. Suddenly the truth dawns on him from their unnatural calm and Billy's inability to hide his feelings.

NOEL

Jesus, he's having a laugh all right.

The coffin appears at the church door with Christine and Lisa in front, dignified. Noel walks quickly out of the church and away. He has lost.

INT. SHOP NEAR BOG – DAY

The Owner is a middle-aged countrywoman.

OWNER

Hello, there, lovely day for it.

The man takes his helmet off. It is, of course, Michael.

MICHAEL

Let me see. Is that tins of corned beef you have there?

He points low behind the counter. The Owner turns and bends to pick one up. As she does, Michael reaches out and slips two bars of chocolate from the display counter into his pocket. Smiles.

OWNER

Yeah, John West. Do you want one?

MICHAEL

Tell you what. Will you hold on to it for me? I'll collect it later on my way back. Save me lugging it around on the bike.

OWNER

I will of course. That's a grand machine you have. I wish I had your speed.

MICHAEL

Ah. It gets me around. Good luck.

OWNER

Bye . . . see you later.

EXT. SHOP NEAR BOG – DAY

Michael gets on his bike and puts on his helmet.

MICHAEL

Fresh air. Culchies. Oh well.

He takes out the stolen bar of chocolate and munches contentedly, imagining . . .

INT. JESUIT COMMUNITY HOUSE – DAY

In the refectory Father Grogan and his fellow Jesuits are sitting down for their evening meal. They bow their heads in prayer before eating. They pay no attention to The Taking of Christ, once again happily oblivious of the treasure hanging on the wall behind them.

EXT. SHOP NEAR BOG – DAY

Michael smiles and flicks away the wrapping of his stolen chocolate bar. Big triumphs, little scams. All in the game.

He starts the Kawasaki and rides off into the countryside.

Cast List

MICHAEL LYNCH	Kevin Spacey
CHRISTINE LYNCH	Linda Fiorentino
STEVIE	Peter Mullan
NOEL QUIGLEY	Stephen Dillane
LISA	Helen Baxendale
TONY BRADY	David Hayman
COMMISSIONER DALY	Patrick Malahide
HARRISON	Gerard McSorley
FR. GROGAN	David Kelly
TOM ROONEY	Gary Lydon
BILLY LYNCH	Paul Ronan
ALEC	Colin Farrel
SHAY KIRBY	Vincent Regan
JEROME HIGGINS	Tim Loane
PETER	Christoph Waltz
BARRY	Bill Murphy
CON	Tony Coleman
LARRY	Barry Barnes
LIAM	Anthony Brophy
LUKE	Paul Roe
GER	Paul Hicky
LENNY	Tom Maguire
DOLE OFFICE CLERK	Joe Gallagher
DE HEER	Herbert Knaup
LORD MAYOR	Alan Devlin
PADRAIG LYNCH	Jer O'Leary
FLINTAN DOORLEY	Hugh B. O'Brien
DESK SERGEANT	Gerard Lee
1ST JUDGE	Conor Evans
2ND JUDGE	Des Braiden
McHALE	Conor Mullen
BRIAN	Enda Oates
NEWS REPORTER	Anne Cassin
RADIO PRESENTER	Dave Fanning

COUNTRY SHOPKEEPER	Ann O'Neill
MAN OUTSIDE BANK	Jonathan Shankey
MR HARMLESS	Bronco McLoughlin
MRS HARMLESS	Angela McLoughlin
MRS HIPPY	Tamzin Shaw
TOMMY LYNCH	Ross Dungan
BREDA LYNCH	Sarah Barrett
SHANE LYNCH	Alex Hayes
EDDIE	Darragh Mullen
NIAMH	Maeve de Blacám
OONAGH	Eva Barrett
JUDGE'S DAUGHTER	Mary O'Driscoll
JUDGE'S DAUGHTER'S BOYFRIEND	Michael Hayes
JOURNALISTS	Rory Egan
	Leonard Hayden
	Brendan Morrisey
	Sarah Pilkington
	Mario Rosenstock

Crew List

Executive Producers for Icon Entertainment International	Ralph Kamp
	Paul Tucker
Executive Producer for Bord Scannán na hÉireann/ The Irish Film Board	Rod Stoneman
Director	Thaddeus O'Sullivan
Producer	Jonathan Cavendish
Screenplay by	Gerard Stembridge
Executive Producers	James Mitchell
	Christine Ruppert
Co-producer	Martha O'Neill
Director of Photography	Andrew Dunn
Editor	William Anderson
Production Designer	Tony Burrough
Costume Designer	Jane Robinson
Original Score Composed by	Damon Albarn
Casting Directors	Ros and John Hubbard
Associate Producer	Margaret Moggan
Finance and Legal Executives	Jonathan Kelly
	Annette Waldron
Script Consultant	Maggie Pope
Production Manager	Dara McLatchie
First Assistant Director	Deborah Saban
Production Accountant	Andrew Lowe
Location Manager	Andrew McCarthy
Production Co-ordinator	Janette Hamill
Assistant Production Co-ordinator	Moyra D'Arcy
Assistant to the Producer	Karen Katz
Assistant to the Director	Ciara Walshe
Assistant Accountants	Adrienne Curran
	Siobhán Southwell
	Orla McGowan
Production Accountant (Germany)	Petra Junk

Dialogue Coach	Brendan Gunn
Unit Publicist	Susan D'Arcy
Stills Photographer	Tom Collins
Publicity (Ireland)	Clarence Pictures
Publicity Assistant	Clare Sweeney
Assistant Location Managers	Michael Casey
	Leanara Frawley
Location Co-ordinator	Rowena Kelly
Second Assistant Director	Marian Barlow
2nd Second Assistant Director	Olivia Lloyd
3rd Assistant Director	Ciara O'Sullivan
Crowd Co-ordinator	Jill Dempsey
Camera Operator	Mike Proudfoot
Steadycam/'B' Camera Op	Keith Sewell
Focus Puller 'A' Camera	Ciaran Kavanagh
Clapper Loader 'B' Camera	Des Doyle
Script Supervisor	Ermer Conroy
Key Grip	Luke Quigley
Playback Operator	Bill Dowling
Gaffer Electrician	Patrick Miller
Best Boy	Vincent Madden
Electricians	Bill Doyle
	Paul Fegan
	Pat Ryder
Generator Operator	Stephen Bruen
Practical Electricians	Des Troy
Sound Recordist	Kieran Horgan
Boom Operator	Noel Quinn
Sound Trainee	Charles Brand
Art Director	Clodagh Conroy
Set Dresser	Dominic Smithers
Property Buyer	Keavy Lalor
Standby Art Director	Richard Fields
Graphic Designer	Lisa Smyth
Draughtsman	Conor Dennison
Storyboard Artist	Romek Delimata
Art Department Trainees	Una Magee
	Frank Monahan
	Kathryn McDonagh
Wardrobe Supervisor	Ger Scully
Assistant Costume Designer	Dulcie Scott

Chief Make-up Artist	Morna Ferguson
Chief Hairdresser	Lorraine Glynn
Property Masters	Triona Coen
	Sam Stokes
Standby Props	Colin G. Mutch
Dressing Props	Christopher Cutler
	Charlie Johnson
	Will Cann
Standby Rigger	James Merrigan
Standby Carpenter	Thomas Burke
Standby Stagehand	Gerard Quigley
Construction Manager	David Whelan
Supervising Carpenter	Paschal Farrell
Carpenters	Brian Geoghan
	David Norris
	Matthew Kirwan
	Michael Murphy
	John Greene
Master Painter	Gerard Richardson
Riggers	Kevin Killeen
	Michael Freaney
Stagehand	John Purdy
Construction Driver	Daithí Curran
First Assistant Editor	Gavin Buckley
Associate Editor	Christine Marier
Conforming Editors	Lionel Johnson
	Celia Haining
Post Production Supervisor	Stephen Law
Score Produced by	Damon Albarn
Music Editor	Terry Delsing
Supervising Sound Editor	Mike Wood
Dialogue Editor	Howard Halsall
ADR Editor	Nigel Stone
Foley Editor	Jupiter Sen
Foley Artists	Jason Swanscott
	Diane Greaves
	Felicity Cottrell
Re-recording Mixer	Paul Carr
Assistant Re-recording Mixer	Robert Farr
Special Effects	Team FX

More Non-fiction from Headline

Lock, Stock and Two Smoking Barrels

GUY RITCHIE

Streetwise charmer Eddy walks into the biggest card game of his life with £100,000 of his own - and his mates' - money. But the game is fixed and Eddy ends up owing half a million to porn king and general bad guy Hatchet Harry. Eddy has a week to come up with the money before he starts losing his fingers to Harry's sinister debt collector, Big Chris - unless he can persuade his dad to hand over his beloved bar instead. Or maybe Eddy and his mates can come up with a better plan . . .

'a hilariously twisted, razor-sharp, comedy gangster thriller . . . *The Long Good Friday* for the *Trainspotting* generation' FHM

'Mixes the authenticity of *The Long Good Friday* with the jet-black humour of *Reservoir Dogs* and the intricately plotted wit of *The Italian Job* . . . one of the funniest films I have seen in years' Neil Norman *Evening Standard*

NON-FICTION / CINEMA 0 7472 6205 5

More Non-fiction from Headline

DARK TRADE
Lost in Boxing

DONALD McRAE

Dark Trade was described by one of the judges of the 1996 Sports Book of the Year as a 'truly wonderful, phenomenal book'. Updated with a new afterword, this is a vivid and compelling examination of the shadowy world of boxing. In a personal five-year odyssey Donald McRae tracks the strange and interlocking lives of the most extraordinary figures in contemporary boxing - from Mike Tyson and Naseem Hamed to Don King, the notorious promoter - and reveals how they are haunted by themes of race and celebrity, poverty and wealth, violence and sex, crime and death.

With unprecedented access to all the big-name fighters as they travel to cities as diverse as Las Vegas and Belfast, *Dark Trade* examines the way in which race and violence beat at the heart of British and American society, and asks what drives men to pursue this most brutal kind of stardom.

'An impressive and powerfully engaging survey of boxing over the past five years . . . a worthy and important contribution to boxing literature' *Guardian*

'Outstanding . . . captures the drama, dedication and inevitable despair' *Daily Telegraph*

'An extraordinary achievement . . . will become one of boxing's standard texts' *Independent on Sunday*

William Hill Sports Book of the Year

NON-FICTION / SPORT 0 7472 5869 4